The

ABC's

Of

Dementia

A Reference Guide To
Your Personal
Dementia Waltz

Tammy Thompson

DEDICATION

This book is dedicated to all of my people, that I have had the honor to dance with during their waltz with dementia. I am ever grateful for the lessons you taught me and the stories you told.

My friends, Judy and Ellen, who really sparked me into writing this, as their Dad danced his waltz. Judy, you were the best dancer he could have ever asked for.

Special thanks to Marilyn for introducing me to Myron. My heartfelt thanks to you Myron for helping me complete the hardest parts of getting this book out there.

.

CONTENTS

JUST A WORD...

If you have picked this book up just to glance through it, you have a person in your life that you think has or might have Dementia. The other reason this book interested you might be because you know you have a person with Dementia. You have already seen the red flags, and now you have and need some answers yesterday!

Have you ignored the little signs that have popped up here and there? Your friend's Dad had dementia. Your person, the person you were thinking about that made you pick this book, is nothing like that. It's just other, different things you are noticing. You are unsure. She is just stubborn, set in her ways, thoughtless, careless, forgetful, clumsy, depressed...the list goes on. Welcome to the Dementia Waltz, because your person will take on their very own, unchoreographed, self-customized dance.

Dealing with Dementia is the most challenging thing you will ever have to do.

Everyone is affected by it, no matter how it touches you. It will be one of the most, difficult, fulfilling, rewarding, exhausting, enthralling, joyful, frustrating, sad and wonderful journeys you will ever accompany anyone on. I call it The Dementia Waltz if you will. It will be slow, graceful, fast, chaotic, beautiful and yet clumsy, confusing and so out of sync when the missteps or stumbles happen.

Please let the anger go, and quit feeling guilty. If you pray, pray for strength, understanding, patience and wisdom. So easily said, right?

I hope you can use this book just as a reference point. I want to address those words that may suddenly become part of your everyday vocabulary as you begin your own personal Dementia Waltz with your person.

These are suggestions and proven techniques that have worked for everyday caregivers. Take away part of it or read it all and refer to it often. Use your own judgment and be creative! It won't hurt!

I will share stories often for you. For reading purposes, I will call my people Molly or Dan. My experiences encompass so many different people and personalities living in memory-care communities. I have had the honor of dancing so many wonderful dances during my career. I would not have changed one moment of it. I hope you grasp the gist... and I hope to offer you a little comfort and maybe some insight for your journey.

Accept help, as hard as that may be. This is so personal. It is as important to be open and loving toward your person, as it is for you to share what you are going through with someone. Doctor, family, friends, your Church, a neighbor. If Church has been part of your and your person's life keep going, it is healing. This dance will become a sleepless marathon at times. You will need support and perhaps you will need to learn how to accept it. You are not alone. There are millions of people out there who are doing their own dance, and do understand where you are coming from.

You will also notice that I have certain words in bold text. Find more on these words through the contents.

I hope you find some ease as you dance with your person.

Tammy

A

Abuse

An ugly word any way you look at it. Physical, Emotional, Financial or Sexual. It is a sickening thought that will make your blood boil, as you **love** and protect your person. The thought of anyone hurting them in an intentional way, because they are defenseless, should make you see red. Mix in the complications of **bad judgement**, **fear**, the changing **mobility**, **falls**, the lying to cover up their mistakes just what can you believe? **Pray** for wisdom and help. **Ask** professionals and friends. Exhaust all your **resources** available, including legal. Contact help with your concerns immediately. Don't **wait** and convince yourself that what you suspect is nothing. Pretend you are **Sherlock Holmes**, look for clues. Your person needs you to take the lead, your dance has begun.

Physical: where are the new bruises coming from? Yes, their skin is very fragile. Try this simple **exercise** to discover just how fragile. Tape a piece of tissue to your arm, (just the 2 ends) and rub down your arm with the other hand firmly. It easily rips and tears. This mock skin is oh so thin, a great example of how fragile they really are. Bumps, scrapes a simple brushing of a door casing can all leave horrible bruises. Accidents do happen. Someone grabbing an arm, hitting, kicking, pinching or your person **falling** will all leave their marks. Your person may minimize the cause for concern, be totally surprised or blame someone for doing it, the options are unlimited. Watch their face closely for **fear**, **anger** or shame as they **talk** to you about it. **Sherlock** follow your gut. Physical **abuse** is tricky and can be unintentionally self inflicted as well.

Emotional: Is their **dignity** being compromised? Are they being reprimanded, scolded, insulted, cussed at, hollered at, called names made to feel stupid, dumb, humiliated as if they were a child? Spoken as if they are deaf and can't comprehend? Does someone speak to your person in a "baby" voice and insult their **integrity**? Is your person blamed for everything, anything, receiving the brunt of someone's **frustration** or **anger**? Is it much easier for someone to say inappropriate things to your person because they can't tell? If they did tell who would believe them? They have Dementia! Ok **Sherlock**, this is a trigger to angry outbursts, refusal to co-operate. They are telling you something, or mimicking behavior shown toward them, perhaps. You can figure it out if you watch and pay close attention. Remember your person was their own decision maker, held a job, ran a company, raised a **family**. They deserve **dignity** and **respect** at all times as they dance their personal waltz with Dementia.

Financial: Is someone taking advantage of them financially? Are they missing **money**? Has your person hidden it somewhere? Has a friend, neighbor, relative accepted **money** from them because they were told of a financial need? Did someone open a credit card in your person's name without them knowing, or fully **understanding** what they are doing? Scammers often target older **people**, they can be easy prey. Unfortunately, **family**, friends, neighbors and **caregivers** can all be taking advantage of your person, not just strangers. The need to help **people** is always there and your person can be taken advantage of easily.

Sexual: Is someone being sexually aggressive toward your person? Is there bruising around their genitals? At their age you certainly do not want to consider it. It can happen more often than you think.

ADL's

Assistance with Daily Living. Waking up, showering, getting dressed, making coffee, going to the bath room, brushing teeth, **eating**. There is so much that we do every morning, without even considering the mechanics. Suddenly your person seems to be having difficulty with some or all of them. Casual excuses might begin as the disease begins. You might notice the frequency increasing. Red Flags are popping up. Are their fingernails long and dirty? Is their lack of personal grooming evident? Does it look like they have not brushed their teeth in a while? Do they wear the same outfit every day? Are they making errors with **medications**? Have they gotten lost just coming home from the grocery store? All of these are signs that there is something going on.

Adult Day Center

A great solution for those who have their person living with them and they need constant **supervision**. Now you can go to work and concentrate on your job. It can become very overwhelming to juggle it all. Work, **family**, Doctor appointments, **caregivers** and all your persons oversight 24 hours a day. Just **breathe**, put on your **Sherlock** and see if there might be some adult day centers in your area. They usually operate much like a childcare care center open Monday through Friday, serving lunch and keeping those who cannot be left alone **engaged** and most importantly safe.

Agitated

Your person is fighting for their sanity. The very inward **frustration** and sometimes **fury** they feel is all consuming. Let them fight. Let them work around it. Find a task that they can be successful at. Remove the jigsaw puzzle that they were drawn to **yesterday** for hours on and off but want nothing to do with today. Bring the laundry basket and **ask** for help folding. Vacuum. Cook. Turn on **music**. Help sort the mail. Look at a magazine with them. Even the men will focus on the right task. It is repetitive **movement; muscle memory** and they can succeed even if you must re-do everything later.

Alcohol Dementia

Very real. This form of dementia can happen to those who are very young, and in fine physical shape. The need for alcohol can become their sole focus. They will lie, steal and run to the nearest bar. An **escape artist** is born. Living in a community with 24-hour **supervision** is the safest option, because now your person even when sober, their ability to care for themselves is gone. They can't manage **money**. They don't eat and grooming is very lax or **clothing** is layered on without the shower. Once they are sober, the need to drink will always be there. The damage to the brain has been done and there is no reversing this dementia. They may seem much better at first because they are sober, however watch close and the evidence of Dementia never went away. Keep an eye out on who visits, even her dearest friend might smuggle a shot or two in for her.

Anger

Yours: You deserve to feel your anger. You have just found out that your person will never be the person you **love** and know. It is only right that you get angry and morn. With any luck at all, your person has discussed this scenario with you and together you have a plan. Or maybe not, and now it's too late, the **decisions** must be made by someone else now, maybe you. You cannot hold anyone with Dementia accountable for their actions. It is useless. They will always have moments of clarity, I am sure of it, they just will not be able to communicate with articulation. It can be wonderful and magical for you when and if you are fortunate enough to be part of the **dementia waltz. Breathe. Pray. Ask** for **patience** and wisdom. Don't blame them, they cannot help it. It is the disease process. They do not act this way because they want to. Be assured that if they had any idea this was who they would become they would be horrified. Don't stay angry, try to **forgive** and **fix it**!. Take the lead. If you can, you may find the Waltz to be an amazing journey together. Once you learn how to lead, or follow your person through this dance, you can gather all the pieces of their life you never knew, as they are revealed.

Theirs: It also can be very emotional if they are angry. Angry at the world, themselves, the doctors, you and even God. Their social barriers may dissolve and they may not hold back **words** or emotions. They may strike out in **anger** and **frustration**. Always keep a 3-foot **bubble** around you for your own protection when they are angry, or if they are angry often they may strike out. Just keep your guard up. Even the tiniest sweetest woman can pack a good punch if she wants. The instant reaction to a disturbing situation for them is usually **fight or flight**. You can be the nurturer, soother the go to person for their comfort. Their dance partner. Just as it is very important for you to work through your **anger** it is important for those with Dementia to express those feelings as well.

Either is not a good experience but you can learn how to minimize the risks. **Listen, eye contact, wait** it out, change the thought process to something new and unconnected. **Wait**.

Molly was in an unusually bad mood. Someone had taken the magazine she was looking at and had been carrying around all morning. She was watching the man walking away from her with her magazine clutched tightly in his hand. Molly was ranting a long string of **word salad** *and obviously furious, started after him. "Molly there you are!" I exclaim walking slowly toward her but intercepting her path. " You won't believe what I have to show you!" My voice gets softer as I get closer. I on purpose stand blocking her sight of the offending thief. "I just got these new earrings and I was wondering if you like them. What color would you call this stone, blue or green?" This was an easy distraction for her knowing how much she loves her jewelry. "We can go to your room and put your earrings on?" I suggest reaching for her hand, and we begin walking toward her room. Success!!*

Approach

If you learn anything from reading this, I hope that it is that you need a soft approach. I promise you it will make all the difference in the world. No one likes to be startled or yelled at. Hearing may be gone or eyesight is fading. Going to an eye doctor is not an option because they can't really answer any **questions** accurately. You can always try but **understand** that it may not be a successful appointment. Their world has become scarier every minute and they need to know that you are a person that can be trusted. You must make them **feel** safe, not afraid.

Sudden loud noises got an angry loud response from Dan. He would **sing** *or chant in a deep booming voice almost self soothing. The more* **agitated** *and louder the other residents would get, so would he. I approach him quietly* **talking** *to him directly and make* **eye contact***. I touch his arm softly, drawing his attention to me, invite him to go with me to a quieter place. This could be a great solution, and don't hesitate to whisper the invitation, make it sound like this is just between the two of us not those other noisy* **people***. Keep calm, smile and connect always with* **eye contact***.*

This is so very important for them to connect with you. Remember you **love** this person. They raised you or married you. They need you.

Ask

Ask your person for advice. No matter how far the disease had progressed they have that human need to be heard, to be valued, to be **respected**. Ask if the sauce needs more salt, do they think the car needs to be tuned up, are snow tires as good as studded tires, do the cookies need to cool on a baker's rack? Ask them about their first kiss, or their honeymoon. Do they want to **pray**? You have a golden opportunity to find out bits and pieces of your person's life you never knew before. Prompt them with the information you know and watch the stories evolve. Embrace the opportunity. Somewhere with in every story will be grains of the truth and those long-term memories are still in there. Don't be afraid to step back in time. Into their time. Dance your way to their memories and the place in time that this terrible disease has brought them.

Don't ever be afraid to ask your own **questions**. Reach out! **Talk** about it, join a support group. Go to **church**! Call your local support networks and find out what is available to you in your area. Converse with others who are also going through this. It pays to find or become an **understanding** ear.

Assisted Living

Is your person living independently? How **dangerous** is this becoming? There are communities being built as quickly as possible because the baby boomers have arrived, and they will be around for a while. Your person could be enjoying an independent apartment with minimal to no **supervision**, then when needed, to an **assisted living** apartment with a couple of hours of help daily, with an easier transition to a **memory impairment** lock down community all with in the ease of one community. There are home shares, **in home care**, meals on wheels if they can still stay at home. It should always be a priority to give them a sense of independence, a voice, **respect** and the feeling of being valued. Research your local options, there should be more than you think available. Use the **internet**.

B

Baby Voices

Please don't. They have memory loss they are not young **children**. These are the **people** who raised kids had jobs, traveled lived a full life, paid bills, fought wars and awaited retirement just like you and me. They are **still there** just because they respond with **word salad**, they still deserve **dignity** and **respect**. No one like to be spoken to or scolded like a child.

*Molly is in the kitchen taking the dish rag and wiping the counter. She is into repetitive movement and will wipe the same area including the coffee pot for long periods of time. As she reaches for the hot coffee pot her caregiver just notices her. "Molly sweetie, don't touch that! It can burn you. No, no, no! It's hot" she says in the sugary voice some **people** use with small children. Molly, a Professor from an Ivy League college, most likely thinks there is a child in the room. She ignores her, or is becoming **agitated** with unexpressed **anger** at being belittled. She reaches for the hot coffee pot and a **dangerous** game of tug of war is now going on. Instead, if her caregiver had said, "Hey Molly, check this out over here" picking up the closest thing, newspaper, salt shaker, keys anything to divert her attention. "Are these your keys? I think that coffee pot could be hot. I don't want it to burn you. I would like a cup, do you want one? If you take these keys I will pour one for us!" reaching for the coffee pot and hand her the keys at the same time. **Bait & Switch.** Suddenly she is **redirected**, in a gentle way, not demeaning her.* Watch her **anger** flare up if you try to forcefully remove the coffee pot from her hands, demanding she give it to you. That makes you the bully on the play-ground and no one likes a bully.

Bad Judgement

This also will happen. Your person will have it. It can be a **red flag** something is going on; it may be your first clue. Are they buying odd things? Do they leave kitchen towels on a hot stove? Do they over tip, suddenly? Are they more forgetful lately? Have they started decorating for holidays that are months away? Are they hiding things?

Are there clues that make you wonder if something needs to be checked out? Do it. Convince your person to go to their Doctor. Go with them, for support and your own answers.

This may be the only time you can have a discussion about their future with them. The earlier the better, no matter how difficult it is.

Bait & Switch

The act of diverting your person's attention from something to something else. If your person is **feeling** sad, scared, **dangerous**, inappropriate or frustrated help them out. Try to get their focus elsewhere onto something interesting and safer.

*Molly has come into the cooking program where you are making an apple pie. She reaches over picking up the apple peeler, examines it and picks up an apple core ready to do surgery. Knowing that Molly could definitely not be trusted even with a peeler, I picked up the biggest reddest apple and said "Molly" with a soft excitement "Molly look at this apple! Isn't it beautiful?" I hold it directly in her line of vision. "Here can you hold this for me? I am so glad you just got here, I could really use your help." I hand her the apple, watching as she puts the peeler on the table. "Would you please tell me how much sugar I need for the pie? My hands are all sticky from the apples and I am making such a mess! Could you please **help me**?" And I push the cook book toward her with my elbow as I pick up the peeler. Molly shakes her head no and states "No" as she pushes the book away, but keeping the apple she leaves. Bait & Switch.*

Always try to trade off to something more interesting. "Don't you **love** the color of this apple?" Can I cut you a piece of pie to eat?" Claim that you would like one too, which reminds you... "look over here"... just guide the focus to a safer place. Have a seat and we will all have a taste! Be enthusiastic and enticing. Bait & switch.

Bathing

As dementia progresses it becomes very challenging to bathe your person. Their unkempt appearance might be one of your first clues that your person is struggling with the first dance steps to the waltz. As the disease progresses they most certainly will not be able to do it themselves. Compound this with a real **fear** of water and the challenge is on. It is imperative that the shower is done quickly and as painlessly as possible. Try putting a chair in the shower and hand bars on the wall. You can find these easily. Begin with explaining what you are doing as you are doing it. Turn the water on first so it warms the bathroom. Let them hold a washcloth and do as much as they can for themselves. It is always difficult because you know that you could do it much more efficiently and quickly than this process. Long though it may be and you might get really wet but trust me it is worth it.

Please give him **dignity** and let him do what he still can with **cueing** from you.

Try **singing** while assisting. You are my sunshine, America the Beautiful, Take Me Out to the Ball Game, their favorite hymn, your favorite hymn! **Music** is magical. It will put you both at ease and takes the focus off what you are doing so it eases the embarrassment for both of you. If singing just isn't your thing, try some **conversation**. Tell a story about something you saw today or thought of or remembered.

The first time I helped bathe Molly and wash her hair there were 4 ***people*** *that had to hold her down on a bed to wash her up. Getting her into the shower was impossible. My heart broke for this poor woman whose verbal skills were non-existent and she was terrified, fighting and kicking. I knew that next week it would be a different scenario. I* *insisted that I take her into the bathroom by myself. I had gathered all her toiletries and assisted her with sitting on the toilet. Then I explained that she would be taking a shower as I turned it on. I took off her* **shoes** *and socks while she was sitting. She fought me some. I handed her a towel and removed her shirt and undershirt.* **Bait & switch.** *She stopped trying to grab the* **clothing** *because her hands were full with the towel. I spoke very softly to her while doing this reassuring her it was okay and she would feel so good after. I pointed out the clean clothes we had to put on after, opened the curtain and let the warm air from the running shower out. I touched the water and then touched her hand. The most difficult part was removing her slacks and underwear then guiding her into the shower. She would not sit but still had the towel I handed her. She began scrubbing me with it. She let me wash her as she washed me and the whole time I got drenched with her soaked towel. I didn't care, if she had been terrified, it was only for a moment. The smile and gentle pat she gave my cheek when we were done was one of those amazing moments I will always treasure.*

Be Aware

From the first signs that alert you things aren't right. Notice, pay attention. Never accuse or be harsh, just curious, soothing and kind. **Ask questions**, yet don't push. Sound casual and concerned not accusing and aggressive. Turn into **Sherlock Homes** and watch for evidence of decline. Your person may just need checking on but don't settle for a false sense of security and **let it go**. If you have even the smallest inkling move on it. Keep an eye out and watch for changes.

Bedding

Make sure they are comfortable and warm enough. Give an extra pillow to support those tender joints. Be careful of **pressure points**, as you lay in the same position for long periods your skin begins to break down. Lower the bed if your person is **falling** out of it when they try to get up during the night. Side rails are also an option and can be very helpful. Your person can help pull themselves up, along with the security of **holding on** when being lowered. Some **people** will even need a mattress on the floor. This is only for severe **fall** risk people and assisting them with getting up will be difficult. Professional facilities use 2 **people** and/or a **Hoyer lift**. Perhaps they have begun **sleeping** in a recliner. Let them be comfortable. I knew a man who preferred a bean bag on the floor.

Bedtime

This is where **routines** are very helpful. New **medications**, the need for more **napping** the many changes going on in your person's body will indeed mess with their **sleeping** habits. Their bedtime will need to be flexible. Days and night can get confused. Your person may be an **insomniac**, or **sleep** all the time. **Ask** about medication interactions.

Behaviors

Your person will shock you with some of their behaviors. They may become physically aggressive, verbally abusive, uncontrollably needy or angry and obstinate. They are trying to tell you something! Be **Sherlock Holmes** and pay attention, you can figure it out. Do they need the bathroom?

Are they hungry or thirsty? Coax them into sitting in a quiet place and have a cookie or drink. Play some soft **music**. **Sing**.

*Molly has been living in a community for a couple of years. She is very mobile and walks around quite a bit. There are a couple of other residents that she has gotten into physical confrontations with. Not throwing punches but growling, cussing at and shirt grabbing and when you looked in her eyes you knew this situation had to be diffused and quickly. My **approach** is calm, and very slow but deliberate. I spoke to her directly and asked her to please tell me what happened to upset her so. She sputtered a few **words** and tightened her grip and gave the other resident a small shake. I put my hands over hers and held her hands very gently pulling her away, encouraging her to hold my hands instead. Still focused on her I say, "Hey Molly, I'm so sorry." I glanced around and because the room was noisy and several other residents were focused and curious I decided to try to remove Molly from the situation. "Come with me, we can **talk** about it, but it's a little too noisy here. Please **help me**, I know where we can go" and the whole time I held her hand, put an arm around her giving a little hug and guided her away from the situation and others, **talking** to her the whole time. Engaging her.*

For **violent** or **dangerous** actions, a **family** member, hopefully her **POA**, and a Doctor might need to become involved. Document these for her Doctor. It will be very helpful.

Blame Game

We all want to blame something or someone for the life events that go wrong. It is human nature to take things out on the ones we **love** or have to deal with every day. Staff will hear of exaggerated stories about how wonderful you are, or how **mean** or thoughtless you are. They will blame you for the sun coming up and the moon setting. She will blame other residents of stealing from her, she will blame the director of being incomprehensible, and ignoring her.

Bra's

Are they necessary? Really?? With so many sport bra alternatives and camisoles available let that battle go. As your person ages warmth is a priority, so add the layers and no one will know! Consider eye hooks and fragile skin. It's a skin tear **waiting** to happen. Do yourself or the care staff that help dress her a favor and let them go.

Breathe

You must train yourself to take a deep breath before reacting to any situation that needs urgent care. A sudden knee-jerk reaction from you will scare, startle or embarrass your person. Loud noises will scare them, they may drop whatever they are holding or clutch it tighter. Hollering at them, will be-little them and make them feel like a child being scolded. Will their reaction be to rebel? Will they lash back, or withdraw and cower? Will they be humiliated and lose self-esteem or will they shut down? Just pause, take a deep breath or two, or three then react. Remember a soft **approach** will get you further. In through your nose and out slowly through your mouth. Chant **"they can't help it. they can't help it!"** See if that helps.

Bubble

The personal space that we all **respect** usually, finger tips to finger tips, holding your arms straight out. Keep this space between you and your **agitated** person. Because our instincts say **fight or flight**, remember if you are invading their bubble you can be a target. If you must help with **personal hygiene**, getting dressed or trying to remove your person from a volatile situation, keep an eye out for your own **safety**.

Burn Out

Be very careful this does not happen to you. **Ask** for help, share responsibilities of being your person's **caregiver**. You cannot do this all by yourself. You will try. You will become exhausted and stressed. Check into your options. Find out what you have available to you. In-home care, adult day centers, private care givers, and communities that specialize in **memory care**. Be smart, get help for perhaps the most difficult things like bathing, dressing, getting ready for bed, in the afternoons when sun-downing occurs, mealtime. Give yourself permission to find some relief. If you do not take care of yourself, you cannot take care of your person in the best way. They can exhaust you.

*When Molly's **family** moved her into our community you could read the stress, anguish, exhaustion, **fear**, and guilt all over their faces. Molly herself was rude, angry and confused. As we sometimes do, she was focusing every bit of that anger onto her daughters and her husband. She cussed like a sailor. They waited until almost their breaking point before finding help. Don't be that **family**. I promised her daughters that the beauty of the disease and her living with us was that the moment they left, there was a staff of loving care givers that would take Molly's mind off their leaving by reassuring her and **redirecting** her thoughts to a different more positive line of thinking. Promising to come back on Tuesday just makes her anxious you are leaving. This can bring anger, **tears** or **frustration**. The best exit on those visits are to just slip out,* *give a kiss, go to get a cup of coffee. Give staff a heads up, and go. No good byes, or promises to be back on Tuesday. Time makes no sense here for her. Eventually you won't beat yourself up or cry all the way home.*

Business Card

Try to think of something short and sweet that you can hand over to the hair dresser, Doctor, Dentist, waitress etc. Try something simple like...

*"This is my Dad. He has Dementia. He cannot answer your **questions**. Please give him his **dignity** and still **ask** him, and I will assist with the **correct** answers. I am his person. Thanks for your **understanding**."*

It is amazing how much this can help. You must remember not everyone **understands** the needs of someone with dementia so if you can help educate them, more power to you.

Butterfly

The person that your person will become, very different, breathtakingly Beautiful. They must first get tangled in the dementia waltz and then they morph into a much more simple yet amazing version of what they once were. Just a perfect comparison. Help them morph.

C

Caregiving/Caregivers

Wonderful **people** the world cannot do without. You. The world is full of them, professional, licensed, unlicensed, **family**, friends and neighbors. **Ask** at **church**, accept help from them. There are many types of personalities so interview **people**. Have your person meet them. Do they click? Will it be a good fit? **Listen** to your person and not so much what they say but how they say it. Are they pleased to see that person when they arrive? Are they angry or upset after that person leaves. Become **Sherlock Holmes** again. **Pray** for the right help and guidance to find the right person. When there is a great connection between your person and a caregiver, a bond does form. Sometimes the bond can seem stronger than the bond they have with you. It might be, contingent on how much time they are together. This too is ok. Accept the help.

Children

There will come a time that your person will not be able to remember their children's names. You would think that they would never forget their own children, but they do. As they slip further and further into the disease they seem to stop right around 12, 14 maybe 16 years old and all they can remember is mom, dad, maybe sisters and brothers if they were close.

Molly is in her wheelchair **eating** *breakfast like everyone else. She is the community's social butterfly but her verbal skills are becoming limited. Her eyes light up and she offers a million dollar smile and an enthusiastic "Hello" to anyone who says hello or good morning to her. One or two* **words** *she handles just fine so she chirps a cheerful good morning to each person she meets. I give her a warm "Good morning, Molly" to which she responds "Oh, good morning Mother!" That of course always buys her a hug. From that moment on I have always been mother to her.* **I just go with it.**

However, do not ever hesitate to bring grandchildren or the babies around. Nothing will light up a day for everyone when **children** are around.

Church

If your person is a member of a church, continue to take them. The fellowship and sense of belonging is irreplaceable. To be accepted and loved by these peers with their **understanding** will provide self-worth, and a sense of belonging during this time of change and torment going on in their heart and head. They may forget names and **people**, unable to recall many of the church events but they will know how church and everyone there makes them **feel**. So provide fellowship for them. Prayer groups are amazing. Even if your person only had a church background as a child, this may be a very welcome activity now and as the disease progresses.

Dan and his son Peter joined us in a church group at our community. Peter came over and whispered to me that he didn't think Dan would stay for long, he never was very religious. I assured him it was fine, they were welcome no matter how long they stayed. Before you knew it Dan was singing with the group, reciting the Lord's Prayer and even took communion. His son was amazed and the look on his face was pure disbelief. I did not even know he knew the Lord's Prayer!" He whispered. "Good!" I whispered back. "you might be surprised what else you find out about your Dad. Just so you know you two are welcome to all the activities, including church, anytime!"

Clothing

Think about their comfort. They may become fixated on certain articles of **clothing** and fight changing them. Go loose for ease of putting things on. Trust me it will be easier for both of you. Always let them choose, but only give 2 choices at a time. It is ok if their choices don't match. You gave them a little bit of control. They will always be cold, so add a sweater. Easy enough to remove. Texture becomes very important, and jewelry may be played with taken off and lost as will wallets and glasses. Work toward avoiding those things if you can. Your earrings are being fixed, your wallet is on your dresser, you won't need it. today I am paying for everyone. **Bra's**! Are they necessary? Just think about lack of flexibility, and their comfort. Layers are key for keeping warm, a camisole, blouse, sweater add the layers. Keep it simple soft and have room to manipulate. Their skin is becoming so thin and frail. Zippers, grommets and buttons can be **painful** causing **pressure points.**

Common Sense

Use it to make everyone's life easier, especially yours. Your person will tell you things, or do things that will alert you that action needs to be taken. Are they thirsty, hungry, cold or need to go to the bathroom? Observe the whole situation and go with your gut. Recognize that what your person is saying is not what they are really trying to tell you. **Word salad**, but if you become a great listener and become **Sherlock Holmes** you will be able to find the truths of what they are trying to tell you.

Communication

Words, touch, gestures, smiles, **hugs**, notes, **eye contact** and songs! Just do it! Never stop trying to communicate with your person.

*Molly was 101 years old. I created a **wishes and dreams** program for the residents where I worked. Molly had grown up and lived her whole life in a nearby small town. I got approval to take her on a road trip. we packed her in the front seat of the company van. We used a* *lot of pillows since she weighed less than 100 lbs. Molly had become very hard of hearing and mostly nonverbal and it was a glorious fall day in New England, with plenty of scenic mountains painted with fall colors to admire. I was sure that no matter how poor her eyesight had become even the blurs of colors would feed her soul. I began calling out landmarks, store names everything I could to try and make a connection, we drove by her house twice. From the moment we got in the van Molly was alert and looking at the wonder of colors. On the way home I began to sing you are my sunshine, Molly joined in and sang the whole song. We communicated.*

Contradictions

No, you are not going crazy or losing your mind. Your person will effortlessly drive you crazy at times with their contradictions. Remember they have no **short term memory**. **Breathe** and **go with it**.

*Molly was **eating** dinner and every time she drank her juice she winced. Dessert happened to be ice-cream and she would chew each bite and wince in **pain** but continued. I asked her if her tooth hurt. She just looked at me chewing. Molly does your tooth hurt? I asked again **touching** my own cheek and making a **painful** face. "Yes," she answered and nodded. I immediately let the Nurse on staff know, and she came over not 10 minutes later and asked," Does your tooth hurt Molly?" to which Molly responded "No" looking like she had no idea what she was asking for. Remember they live in the moment.*

Your person will give similar responses to you and the dentist! You will find yourself explaining to everyone that your person has dementia. Please don't whisper about him or **talk** about him over his head as if he isn't there. If you do you may have just sabotaged the appointment.

Your person may instantly become "difficult". Their feelings are hurt, no one likes to be whispered or talked about. Carry that **business card**!

Conversation

Have it every chance you get. **Ask** who, where, when, what but never **why**. They can tell you all those things except **why**, because they do not know. And not knowing **why** will frustrate them more than anything. But **talk** to them, give them **eye contact**. **Listen** to what they say. There are some amazing things they will tell you. There will be funny jokes and stories they will share. Their string of **words** may be **word salad**, but their gestures and **facial expressions** and their tone can tell you all you need to know. Go with it. Laugh and smile back at them, frown and look concerned if they need it. Hug them if they are sad and reassure them. **Mirror** the emotion and **fix it**.

Correct

Very rarely will your person be correct, and even worse you will wonder if your choices and **decisions** are correct. They will not, and cannot, be accountable for accuracy and you will never **feel** like you are correct about anything so follow your heart This dance came with no lessons no choreography. You are making this waltz up as you go. Please do not continuously correct your person, it will be insulting to them. **Yesterday** did not happen, they don't remember what they had for dinner, they cannot remember. Therefore, you will always be correct in your recall and this may make them uneasy, making them **feel** incorrect about everything. If they stop **talking** they can't ever be incorrect, right?

It is hard to always be wrong and get corrected by everyone, it seems all the time.

Cry

It's good for you. Anyone who even hints that you should not cry obviously has not joined the waltz yet. Cry all you want. Losing someone to Dementia is one of the hardest things you may ever have to deal with. It is a loss, a long torturous death that you must bear witness to. If you want to cry, just go ahead.

Your person may do it often and you may have no idea **why**. After exhausting the usual needs, physical discomfort, hunger, the need for the bathroom, **pain**, singing their favorite song, etc. Sometimes like yourself **sadness** is just that. Let them cry. Offer a shoulder to cry on or a hug or just hold their hand letting them know through touch that you are there. Be quiet and let it happen. Sometimes it's all you can do, and a little comfort is all they need.

Cueing

This is the art of patiently showing and verbally guiding your person to successfully complete a task.

"Dan, let me show you a trick I know to open the toothpaste. Sometimes it is very hard to open up" at this point Dan agreed handing me the tube. *"Do you like a lot of toothpaste? More than this? I apply a fair amount. "There you go, don't forget to brush up and down, that's right!"* (I show the motion). *"Now rinse, and spit, yep right there in the sink. Now rinse the toothbrush, Good. Here let's keep your toothbrush in this cup."* And Dan followed my **directions**, I paused after each step and assured him he did everything right.

All verbal and visual cues. This will keep it dignified. You may even offer to help hold the brush for them (ie.. cup, fork, cookie, hairbrush, paintbrush...you get the idea.). Take the toothbrush in your hand, place theirs on top of yours and **talk** your way through it. This lets them do the task with you, instead of because of you. With their hand on top of yours, it feels like they are in control. This makes such a huge difference. Assure them that you **understand** this task can be very difficult for you as well. Together you can **fix it**!

D

Dangerous

In the world of dementia everything can become dangerous. Stairs that your person can **fall** down or up, ill-fitting **shoes**. Scatter rugs become a trip hazard. Driving, how to stop them from doing so? Knives, stoves, people. Everything can become a danger as good **judgement** diminishes with the disease.

De-Hydration

A huge risk for those with dementia. Motor skills and dexterity are going and words become impossible to grasp, so asking you for a glass of water is impossible. Offer something to drink continuously, use easy to hold cups and try to refrain from using sippy cups for **children**. In today's world, there are many options of closed drinking bottles available with some trial and error you will find the right one.

Decisions

Yours will become many. Many more than you want. Medical, financial, housing, **caregivers** and on and on. Theirs will become nonexistent. It will become harder and even impossible for them to decide on anything, so keep it simple. Either or. Yes or no. Blue or red. Hungry or thirsty. It is so important that you keep asking, including them **respectfully** as though they can make those decisions. It is **respectful** and it **validates** them.

Dementia Waltz

My personal definition of being with your person all through their journey of the disease process. It can be graceful, clumsy, fast or slow, angry or funny. It sort of encompasses all the different dances watched with such relish or "Dancing with The Stars." Ballroom, Jive, fox-trot, quick step, tango or freestyle you see what I **mean?** Because the word "waltz" always seemed so sophisticated and classy I **respectfully** refer to this journey as a waltz. The many **people** I danced with, I **respect** and **love**. I was honored to be their partner. I hope you **feel** the same way about your person.

Denial

Very early in the disease denial will become a key factor. They didn't do or say that, just to cover for the fact that they did. They will **fear** that something is indeed wrong but not want anyone to know. How do they feel? Fine, good, tired. You will get the appropriate responses not to make you worry. Just like you, they will search for possible culprits as to why they are "off". They must be dehydrated, coming down with something, too busy to attend **family** function, they have a headache, their knee hurts, arthritis is acting up, they are going to try vitamins. Anything to chase the confusion away. If your person drinks alcohol they may drink more, or you may think they are drinking more, but they aren't. It is the disease process.

I was doing a group activity with 5 or 6 people who have varying stages of dementia when we got into a **conversation** *about how they handled it when they joined the CRC (Can't Remember Crap) Club in earnest. Can't Remember Crap. I asked what did they do to cover up that they were having difficulty. Dan who always loves to give advice insisted that you must get a yellow legal pad, and every night before bed you write down what you need to do the next day or the next week for that matter. You list it then you can cross off your accomplishments. Molly added in that she will call her sister, or best friend to check with them on things she couldn't recall, how to make that pie? How long did she bake hers? When will they go grocery shopping? Who is the plumber they have always used? When did they go out to lunch last? Dan added that he would just agree then quickly change the subject. "People let things go if you agree with them." As a once savvy businessman he warned "You agree but keep it a little vague," "Oh, yes, I was going to put the lawn mower away but I had to rinse the grass off with the hose first and had to take a phone call." Molly blamed leaving the stove on and burning the soup to a crisp on having a* **conversation** *with a neighbor out in the yard. So many reasons why things go wrong.*

Depression

Serious and undertreated in those with Dementia. As your person goes deeper into the disease, they know that something is wrong. They may take it out on those around them, (or themselves) Arguments about who did not do what was promised, excuses for **forgetting**, never wanting to commit to anything. They may internalize it, blaming a cold, their arthritis, a headache, upset stomach, just too tired to do anything. Depressed, of course. Treated? Most likely, not.

How can they **talk** to a professional about their depression when they cannot grasp the **words** to express their **feelings?** **Why** go to a doctor, when they are terrified what he might find? Go to appointments with your person, mention concerns you have. See what is available to your person in your area. Find a **Geriatrician.**

Desire/Desperation

Our human needs and desires become so very intense with this disease that there are no holds barred. You may be the target of this need, you may witness the flirtations and physical side, the inappropriate comments and touches. Just taking what is wanted without consideration of paying for it, or if it belongs to someone else. This is a perfect time to use the **Bubble.**

*Molly had just been moved into a **memory care** facility where she had freedom to roam anywhere in the building. All outer doors were locked with a coded touch pad to unlock them. Molly rattled every door she could find, over and over again. She was desperate in her desire to find a way out. There was nothing to deter her. She would watch visitors using the key pad trying to grasp the numbers to memory. She would randomly push buttons on it hoping to find the code. Her **determination** was fierce. Sometimes **food** would deter her, asking for her help with a project would work better. Remember the need to have **purpose** never goes away.*

Destructive Behavior

First you have to know that your person is just trying to tell you something. They are angry or frustrated, hungry, did they lose something? Are they being harmful to someone else or themselves? Does it happen at certain times of the day or at certain places or toward certain **people**? Are **medications** being taken correctly are they dehydrated?

Dan was taking things out of his dresser, ripping at buttons and trying to tear the sleeves of various shirts. "Dan, hi. I came to see if you could **help me** *with something?" I* **approach** *slowly giving* **eye contact**, *offering my hand and leading him to the dining room table. I gather recycling mail and place it in front of him. "I need to tear these up, could you* **help me?**" I **ask** *as I pick up an envelope and tear it in two. I hand Dan half and I tear my own half,* **waiting** *for him to tear his. He frowns, examines his piece and slowly rips it into two. I smile and give him a fresh piece, which he tears quickly, a small smile beginning to form on his mouth and eyes. He tears the next piece slowly, seeming to enjoy the sound. The next one is torn fast and loud. Everybody loves to rip paper, it makes babies laugh, kids* **love** *it, adults find it soothing. Find a creative outlet for the destructive behavior! Dig a hole in the garden, throw a ball for the dog.*

Determination

Their focus can be intense. You have no idea what determination is until your person is in the mid-to-end stages and becomes focused on going through a door (for a reason and with a **desperation** only they **understand**) and you are trying to stop them. Have you ever seen a story about a mother lifting a car off her child? Well let me tell you superhuman strength is very real. Huge pieces of furniture can be lifted and thrown by the tiniest frail person. It is amazingly mind boggling. I strongly recommend that you think quickly on your feet, play **Sherlock** and have practiced your re-direct skills. You can swiftly take the focus off the **desired** object. Sometimes for the need to be heard and acknowledged you may have to let them through that door and walk with them. It may or may not be far, so be ready. Just have faith that this is something that your person needs to do.

Molly is a vibrant New Yorker, always dressed to the nines, and never leaves her room without lipstick. She had attended a couple of meetings that I held with the residents about starting a resident based newspaper, to be written in their own **words**. *Molly decided that she could perhaps write a story or two for it. The paper became a much larger project than I had anticipated. Molly would agonize over her writings the whole month. She very quickly went from 1 story to 4, and she would do research at the library, bring me photo's to be included, she was* **Engaged**. *Molly would sit at the door to the employee entrance and* **wait** *for me to come into work. "Tammy, Tammy, Tammy!" She would exclaim when seeing me, she had changes, was checking to make sure I had typed the changes correctly, did I have all her stories. I would breathe, relax and spend however many minutes it took to soothe her concerns. Her worries were all consuming for her. It was urgent for me to* **fix it**. *To make sure things were perfect. Then she could relax then think up some new ideas for the next month's edition.*

I gave her a writer of the year award at our 1 year anniversary party and she ever so proudly displayed it in a prominent spot on her wall. It was my hope that her **family** *will enjoy all her writings. They were indeed beautiful thoughts and feelings she shared. We collected and typed them especially for her binder that she kept along with each edition of the paper. She was a treasure to work with although when 2 or more employees warned me she was looking for me before I even entered the locked community, I often wanted to sneak in a different way! At least take my coat off and drop off my pocketbook before finding her. But then I would remember* **why** *I began the paper, to get our residents involved. So, with a smile and a deep breath I would meet her head on.*

Dignity

One of our innermost **desires** that never goes away. We all want to be dignified, **respected**, and **validated**. We will fight tooth and nail to keep those very basic human needs. We have come a long way and deserve to be **respected**. Please keep that foremost in your mind and heart while dancing with your person. They spent many years earning the right to be treated with dignity, so make a pledge to do so. It may become difficult to honor that promise. It may help to keep reminding yourself of an instance that you will forever remember of when they were strong, sharp and accomplished an impossible task, or managed to handle a very difficult decision or situation. They are still that person! Please treat them with dignity. Don't comb their hair into pigtails with ribbons and tell them how adorable they look, when they only ever wore a French braid.

Direction

Written or verbal. Don't be afraid to give direction as it is **needed**. Keep it simple, direct one step at a time. Write Notes if they are avid readers. I have seen **people** who have become non-verbal will read things out loud and perfectly. Part of the newspaper, signs, name tags, menus, pages from books. You can label doors or post pictures. The bathroom door is a great place to begin. Write out their night time routine for them. Use pictures, a toilet on the bathroom door may help.

Don't Give Up

Go with it. Don't ever give up, you can give in, but don't give up. Go with your person to whatever time and place they are living today. It is giving back that unconditional **love** that your parents gave to you as a child needing help and guidance. You will never know if you will be waltzing a fox trot, doing a samba, quick step, tango, or a little freestyle! Just enjoy the dance.

E

Eating

People love to eat. **Food** will become the event that your person looks forward to every day. It is a social function.

This can become very interesting. **Tastes** will change. Food they used to hate they may try again and find they **love** it. They may eat incredibly fast causing **fear** of choking. They may only be able to handle finger **foods**, sandwiches. The dexterity needed to manipulate a fork or spoon may just not be there anymore. You can use the hand under hand technique and this is helpful. They have the **feeling** of guiding you as you help them. Place your hand on the cup and theirs over yours as you guide the cup to their mouth. It puts your person in control. Incapable today doesn't mean that tomorrow they can do it perfectly. Always **encourage** them to try, it lets them keep their **dignity** and **self-respect**.

Either/Or

For your own sanity only give your person 2 choices either, or. They will not be able to grasp the concept of deciding between 3 choices any more. That will only frustrate them and you. Keep it simple, for them and yourself!

Encourage

Every chance you get. Encourage and reassure. Everyone needs it and your person needs it x 10. Make their memories, tasks, **conversations, music, church** positive. If you provide **conversations,** tasks etc.. that your person with encouragement be successful at, that is a beautiful thing.

Engage

The art of keeping someone interested. Whatever it is, TV, a book, a craft project, a football game, **conversation**, the list goes on. It is a talent you will find useful in all aspects of your life, and a talent that will give you many enjoyable hours with your person. Your person will always be at their best when being engaged. Aren't we all?

Escape Artists

I take my hat off to every one of them. If this part of their thinking process is working, I say good for them! Your **Sherlock** will be on overtime.

Molly had a tight group of 3 other residents that she would hang with every day. They were very smart a lawyer, engineer, communications specialist and Molly worked at an auto dealership. One day the lawyer, engineer and communication specialist removed the window from its casing on a far wing of the building. Molly meanwhile removed a second window on the opposite side of the building. The 3 were noticed by staff immediately, and as protocol called for, a head count began. Shortly the other window was found and by the time the headcount was finished and Molly was confirmed missing only 15 minutes had gone by. Molly meanwhile had climbed out the window and scaled the fence. She walked 6 city blocks to a convenience store, convinced the girl behind the counter to call a cab for her, rode 20 miles to the auto dealer that she knew well, convinced them she'd forgotten her wallet at home, asked them to cover her cab fare and called her son to come get her. It only took 30 minutes. By this time the police were called and a missing persons report was put *out, Molly's **POA** was called, and confirmed he was bringing his mother back. The best escape ever. Fortunately a safe escape. Not all go that way.*

Exercise

Keep their bodies **moving**, stretches, walks dance, whatever you can get them to do. They will feel so much better. Use upbeat '50's or '60's rock and roll or country to exercise to. **Music** is magic. The more fit they are the longer they can dress themselves, feed themselves, wash themselves, walk with a steady **gait**. Be as self sufficient as possible.

Eye Contact

You have to use it. Even the person near the end of this journey will make connections through eye contact. It is a must. They will connect with you and form a bond if you offer eye contact when speaking with them. If they live in a community they may have unfortunately gotten used to being **talked** over, around and about while they are right there. They are **still there**! They deserve your full attention.

F

Facial Expressions

You have to watch them closely. Are they sad, angry, frustrated, worried, concerned, happy, excited and loving? You will recognize these and more as you progress with this disease. Respond accordingly, it is as easy as that. **Breathe**. Then **mirror** the emotion until your person shows comfort and then change the path of their thought process, move the **conversation** into a better **direction**, somewhere that brings on a good feeling.

Falls

They do happen. They will happen. They are incredibly scary. Physically their body is changing causing trouble with balance. It is extremely scary because of the brain shrinkage that accompanies the disease process. The average brain weighs three pounds. By end of the disease process it can shrink to half of that leaving a lot of room to bounce around in a skull, making it difficult to detect swelling. Canes walkers, wheel chairs may become necessary. Reminding them to use these will become a new challenge, so try personalizing their walker for easy recognition. Put their name on it, a silk flower or a bright ribbon.

Family

Who are they? Your person will lose the connections. Care staff will be called, mother, father, sisters, cousins, the list goes on. Granddaughters will be pretty girls who are nice. Grandsons will be that boy from high school. Daughters are bossy women always making a fuss. Family becomes anyone who makes them feel safe.

Fear

This will become more and more evident during the disease process. It will grow as their memories slip away, so they will focus on the memories they do have. At the beginning of the disease the fear comes out in **anger**, finding blame in others, defensive **denial**. There are more arguments now, tasks get delegated to **people**. Lists are being made. You will wonder what is going on, is it **depression**, how long before they come out of it? At mid-stage, they feel fearful you will go away. They know they cannot live without you. You will become their lifeline. They are afraid that if they do something wrong you might abandon them. Put them in a terrible nursing home to die. At end stage, they are possibly in a community with others. They have lost everything. Everyone is a stranger, there is no privacy, their things may disappear, there are **people** they don't like.

Molly is deep in the end stage. She is wheelchair bound, and holds onto 3 beanie baby bears in the crook of her left arm. She croons and coddles them. She is contentedly settled to a very young 11 or 12 in her memory recall. She can't remember her adulthood, her husband or **children**. *She knows everyone is much older than she is. For the most part she is always very sweet. As her sun-downing begins she gets panicked that she has to go home. Her Father will be furious at her if she isn't home before dinner. We reassure her it is okay, he was called and he said she could stay for dinner. Just a fiblet to put her at ease. It works but she is a little doubtful. After dinner, her anxiety rises and there is genuine* **fear** *almost terror in her urgency to leave and get home. I tell her to* **wait** *right there for me and I leave her line of vision. After just a few minutes I come back very excited with slightly exaggerated happiness and say "Molly, I just called your Dad on the telephone and asked him if you could please have a* **sleep** *over tonight if I being you home in the morning and he said yes!!" She is very doubtful, I have not fixed it yet, so I have a* **conversation** *about how we will put our pajama's on, eat ice-cream, watch a movie and* **talk** *about boys! I have 2 beds so she can have her own. We could play* **music** *if she wanted. As I am painting a vivid picture of the fun time we will have I can see how she is beginning to relax, and when she smiles at me its magic. No teeth, eyes shining and delight written all over her face she asks if we could have root beer. I assure her of course. If she goes and gets ready I will be in in about 1 hour with the root beer and ice cream, I give her a big hug like a* *best friend would and she goes happily off with her caregiver. About 1 hour later I check on her and she is sound asleep hugging all 3 bears.*

Feel

Your person will want to touch everything. Does it feel the way it looks? They may stroke a blanket, reach to touch a stranger's silk scarf in public. Supply your person with things to touch, a treasure box full of **textures**. How they feel is very different. They won't be able to find the words to explain it, so everything might just be "bad" or "terrible" or "awful", without details.

Fight or Flight

Fight your way through it, or run for your life.

Fiblets

Fiblets are the untruths that we tell those who suffer dementia to put them at ease. This is a technique I use personally, "fiblets" is not a real word. Reassurances if you will. It is our chance to convince them we would **love** to help with their concern, whatever it is be creative. Don't promise outrageous things you will lose their trust. They still make **judgements** of character and follow their gut. Give plausible solutions and double back to let them know it is done if need be.

*Dan is in his wheelchair in the hallway asking everyone he sees if they know where his car is. He has a meeting and he can't find his car. Care staff as they go by him respond that they haven't seen his car but the more time that passes that no one helps him the more **agitated** he gets. He is hollering now out of **frustration**, and rolling in every one's way trying to get someone's full attention I **approach** him softly "Hello*

Dan," I am pulling up a chair next to him. "What's going on? Anything I can help with?" I **ask** giving him **eye contact**. He sizes me up and says "I can't find my Damn car, no one around here has seen it. I think it's been stolen. Have you seen it? It's red, a ford." I think hard for a moment and say "Wait isn't this Tuesday? Sue took it to have the tires rotated, and an oil change. Sue said she would have it back first thing in the morning." He thinks for a moment, shakes his head and says, "Oh damn it I have that meeting at 2 today. How am I supposed to get there? Can you give me a ride? I'll pay you." He asks me, so the real problem has surfaced. "Oh, I thought your wife, Sue, said it had to be on Wednesday, the guy couldn't make it today so that's **why** she scheduled the oil change and stuff for today. Look at that, you have the afternoon free. You know they are baking cookies this afternoon, can I interest you in supervising? That way you get the first warm cookie." A perfect **bait & switch**. "Might as well, things get changed around here and no one tells me a thing." He mutters but heads for the activity room. **Zen**.

Fix It

Whatever it is just fix it. Even if that means giving in. Do they insist on **holding on** to their plate after lunch? Let them. Are they angry at someone or about something in the room? Guide them to a different place a different object to ease their anxiety. Give them a hug assure and soothe them. Are they hungry? Tired? Thirsty? (If they are trying to drink the water out of a flower vase they are thirsty, or trying to eat a flower they are hungry). Pay attention to what might be poisonous. In a light gentle way tell them that that probably doesn't **taste** very good, but I will get you some juice or a cookie that will be much better. Don't be surprised if they insist on **holding on** to whatever delicacy they have chosen until you make a trade.

Molly was practically hysterical. She sat in her wheelchair, sobbing and begging for someone to help her. "My teeth," she kept crying out getting louder and louder for each nurse or caregiver who walked by. She had worked herself into a frenzy and now was crying real **tears.** *I took a deep breath (see* **breathe***) and swooped in very concerned and asked what was wrong! I deliberately pulled up a chair and sat with her at eye level and gave direct* **eye contact.** *She poured out her story about how her teeth were" wrong, "they needed glue here," and she drew a line down her cheek to the corner of her mouth, "and here," she did the same to the other cheek "and here," and drew that nail straight under her bottom lip. She was shaking now, she was so upset. At that moment, a young lady I worked with told me she had redone her denture 3 times and they could not do it again. I looked at Molly and offered to fix it for her. I took her to a quiet private place. I told her I needed her dentures so I could clean them. She took them out herself and handed them to me. I soaked them in warm water and made her a coffee and two pieces if toast. I asked her to eat the toast and it would get rid of any residual glue left in her mouth. She ate the toast questioning each half. I would nod and reassure her she needed to eat it all, and drink the warm coffee because this loosens the glue. As she ate she calmed down and was much more agreeable. I cleaned her teeth until all signs of glue were gone, and dried them thoroughly. I urged her to finish her coffee and make sure all the* **food,** *crumbs and glue were gone. She agreed, and I let her* **help me** *put the glue on her teeth to her specifications and we placed them in her mouth. She seemed surprised at how good they felt and with the relief in her eyes and smile on her face I had just made a* **magic moment** *for her,* **problem solved.**

Flirty

It will be hard to see but your person may become very flirty toward someone else or even fixated on a person (**caregiver**, staff member if living in a community or another resident.) It can be hard watching your spouse or father flirt or say something suggestive to a young care staff. Or you might walk in to visit your husband and find him walking down the hall holding hands with another resident. Your Parent might flirt with you. We all like to flirt. It feels good. So try to smile your way through it and blame the disease, not them.

Food

Just as soon as you prepare your person's favorite foods, you could find they will not eat it. They hated squash their whole life and you observe them enjoying it, no loving it. They may need to have their diet changed to mostly finger foods if manipulating a fork or spoon becomes too difficult. Remember to give them as much **dignity** as you can while **eating**, make it easier for them to accomplish that simple task of feeding themselves. Finger **foods** can work for a while, but watch for choking hazards, and toward the end of the disease, pureed foods in a blender. Many communities will offer molds of the puree food, so that peas look like a pile of peas, not just a rationed scoop. Sugar is a gateway for drinking and **eating**, sweet things like ice-cream, yogurt and pudding are usually always welcome treats. Sometimes dipping foods in ice cream will convince your person to eat. Use a **clothing** protector that covers the front of their shirt as spilled and dripped food will happen. This will help slow **clothing** changes.

Forgetting

The more they do the more you have to **Let it Go**. Your person is fighting their own daily inner battle with forgetting. They will sense your **frustration** and **anger** at their inability to remember things, and act out accordingly. **Tears**, withdrawal, **anger**, **fury**. They will beat themselves up about it. Their memories will be unreliable and backwards in time. Of course they do not remember their granddaughter, they are only a kid themselves, and suddenly feeling scared. You just told them they are old, they want their mom and dad.

Forgive

It is a must. You will never get a sensible explanation or well-deserved apology. For that to happen, your person must know why they did what they did, said what they said or reacted the way they reacted. With dementia your person will never know why. That part of their brain and **reasoning** is gone.

Frustration

Yours: you will need a sympathetic ear. **Family**, your minister, priest, Rabbi, a support group, your best friend, the **caregiver** you have had to hire. Vent. Vocalize your frustration .Don't take it out on your person. Their frustration will be yours to turn around. So not only do you have deal with your own, but try to fix their **feelings** of frustration.

Fury

You may never believe the fury that can erupt so suddenly from a person sinking into their dementia. It can be frightening to say the least. This is where you will be tested to use every soothing technique you know, and you will wish for more. Remember **music** is magic, and sometimes you just need to ride it out. It takes a lot of adrenaline to have these furious moments, and when they subside hopefully your person will be tired and worn out from the exertion.

*Dan was in a tear, he was throwing his sheets off his bed, wiping the end table clear, trying to pull pictures off the wall. He sat in his chair and began ripping pages out of his book about Alaska. I got him a swimming pool noodle and balloon and we hit it with all the **anger** he had pent up until he was tired.*

G
Gait

It always amazed me how physically fit most **people** I have encountered with dementia (early stages) are. They are on the move, with nowhere to go. This will diminish without a doubt. **Shoes** will become an issue and the unsteadiness will most likely find them at the end of their lives in a wheelchair. **Muscle memory** plays a big part in their **mobility**.

*Dan was a military man, avid sail boater and skier. He walked always on a mission holding something tight to his chest in a death grip and walked only forward. He would often get stuck in corners, unable to figure out how to turn around. I was coming up a hallway and saw him headed my way. 1/2 way between us slept another very long legged resident sprawled out in a wing backed chair. I knew before I could get there to assist Dan around the obstacle, he was going to trip and **fall** onto the **sleeping** resident. In my mind's eye I saw him trip, **fall** and land on the end table crashing into the wall and no telling what injuries would happen to either of them. I knew better than to holler out a warning that would only startle them both, and really make it worse.*

Dan stumbled and did only what I could call a jiggly jump landed on his feet and continued on his mission. It was another amazing moment.

Gait Belt

You may need to use one to help your person stand and walk. This simple tool will help prevent unwanted injury from pulling or tugging on arms. Remember how frail skin and muscles get with age.

Geriatrician

A Doctor specializing in Seniors and ageing.

Go With It

Your person will say things that might embarrass you because it is TMI, inappropriate for the environment you are in, what they have put together for a sentence makes no sense at all, or suddenly they put the magazine they were reading or the napkin they were holding on top of their head. You do not know how to react; do you say something in response? Do you **correct** them? Do you hurry them out of the store? Do you react like a humiliated teenager? No, just give in, change the subject drawing their attention elsewhere or go with it. laugh too, put a napkin on your own head.

H

Hand Holding

Safe and secure. Do it. Touch is under estimated. Your mother soothed you by stroking your cheek when you were a baby. As a toddler, your hand was held for protection. As a teen, you held hands out of friendship and **love**. In marriage, we hold hands in comfort and closeness. In dementia, we hold hands for all those things and more.

Haves and Have Nots

Is it safe? Can they eat or drink it? Can it break and leave sharp pieces? Nail files Nail clippers, tools, scatter rugs, you will need to take inventory constantly. Jewelry may need to be locked up and saved.

Molly was very hungry and eyed a bowl of apples banana's and oranges. She chose an orange and walked away with it, not remembering how to peel it and ate the whole thing skin and all. She was hospitalized, placed under nursing **supervision** *as her body tried to recover from the toxicity the peeling gave her gastro system. Who knew an orange could be considered an unsafe* **food**?

Head Phones

If your person will wear them this a beautiful way to mend their soul with **music**. If they insist on taking them off and dis-assembling them they may not be a very good idea.

Help Me

Many **people** will repeat this over and over with no solution in sight. Remember they are fighting an invisible battle. They are lost. They are lonely. They are scared. They can become desperate with need. They don't know **why**, or what would make them feel better. They may only be able to **cry** out for help, to anyone walking by. One on One time is about all you can do. Get them involved in anything that works, **pray**, a puzzle, painting, reading, fixing something, cooking something, walking go for a ride whatever eases their soul. Remind them of their worth, how smart, amazing and beautiful they are.

Hire Help

Find some relief. If you work and try to manage your own **family** while trying to manage a person with dementia, you will not be able to do it for long. Take breaks, interview **people** and hire help. This will be reminiscent of finding child care for your babies. Use your insights and play **Sherlock** again. Find someone your person likes and hire them to get some relief, ease your stress.

Hoarding

This is a form of control. As your person begins to lose their **words**, thought process etc. they will fight to gather and hold onto anything they can. They may gather random things and hide them in the closet or dresser drawers. Instead of stopping them observe the pattern. Put your **Sherlock** on and see where the hiding places are. Check them frequently, because **food** will also be hidden.

Molly grew up in England and saw many wars. She was very thrifty and an excellent cook. Her favorite memory was cooking dinner for the US Navy men and their superiors. After the meal, the Captain made his way to the kitchen demanding to know who made the biscuits for dinner. Timidly she stepped forward and said "I did." The Captain looked down at her as she stood before him all of 5-foot-tall, reached out to shake her hand and said "That was the best tasting biscuit I ever ate. Thank you." Molly looked up at him and said very seriously "I have more, would you like another?" To which he laughed and said "Yes, I want at least a dozen!" With a blush Molly gathered them up for him.

*As she settled into our community She quietly withdrew. She was quite clever however. And knew that we kept a supply of ice cream cups in our freezer. I saw her one day help herself to one, which was ok and not really an issue. A few days later I was walking by her in the hall, I said "Hi Molly! How are you?" She looked up at me smiled and said "Fine" with a nod. At that moment, I realized she was **eating** a pilfered ice cream that had melted who knows when, with a pencil she always had in her walker for her word searches. I realized she had not figured out where we kept the spoons and was making due. Immediately I said "Molly let me go get you a fresh frozen ice cream and spoon. It will **taste** so much better." I reassure her, come back and make the exchange. A few days later I went to go remind her we were having **musical** entertainment and she should come to the activity room. I found her sitting in her room looking out the window. She readily agreed to come with me but thought she **needed** her sweater. I searched her closet but it wasn't hang there so I asked if I could look in her dresser. She agreed and as I searched I found it along with 3 melted un opened ice cream cups, packages of crackers and a pastry they had offered at breakfast 3 days ago.*

She was hoarding **food**.

Holding On

Your person will hold on by the skin of their teeth.

*Molly is pleased we came to visit her. She was dressed up a little and surveyed the table spread with her favorite **foods**, a real celebration. She delved into a piece of butterflied shrimp and giggled. "I am so glad you are here." Sipping her ginger ale. Her gaze looked around the room, others on wheelchairs or using walkers. Care staff buzzing around with a careful sense of urgency. "I really don't belong here" she whispers. "I was lucky, oh look there is my boss!" She is looking at a young male caregiver who paused to speak to a resident. "He gave me the day off*

45

because he knew you were coming." She leaned in closer and whispered *"I am only here for the money you know." "Well I am glad he gave you the day off, try the broccoli it is really good."* I **encourage** *her bringing her focus back to her lunch. It was much later I remembered that she used to work at a lodge in upstate NY. She lived there and was the wait staff for the summer, she was 19 years old. This is her way of holding on, her* **reality**.

Hoyer Lift

A machine used to lift your person onto the bed toilet or into the bath. Not everyone will need to be moved with this machine. However, those that are too heavy to lift manually even with 2 **people** will need this equipment. It can be a scary experience unless your person really trusts those using it. Weight is not the only time it is needed. I have seen residents who become so fragile that manual movement hurts them so much a hoyer is a better choice to assist them up and down on a bed, or in the shower.

Hugs

Priceless. Human contact is healing, soothing. In a world of dementia **people** around you look at you differently, **talk** as if you don't exist even if you are in the room. They are forced to live with strange **people** they do not know or even like. Hugs keep you grounded. They say I **love** you and you are so very important to me. Not just the customary hello and goodbye hugs we all **feel** obligated to give but the heartfelt hugs that say you are amazing.

Hum

Next best thing to singing. It is **music**. Your person is not judgmental, can you carry a tune, are you flat or sharp? Trust me, I always said what I lack in talent I make up for it with enthusiasm. Just as with everything in life practice makes perfect.

I

Imagination

If your person was imaginative in any way, keep it alive. **Exercise** their Brain. Are they religious? Imagine God and heaven. Imagine you are going to the airport and you can get on a plane fly anywhere you want to go, where? You are building your dream home, what kind of roof would you put on it? What favorite movie star would you have lunch with right now? Robert Redford? Paul Newman? Elizabeth Taylor? Would you rather fly in a plane or take a train? Where would you go? Just imagine the possibilities.

Importance

Yours and theirs are two very different things. Give them **respect** they so well deserve. Is it worth the battle of taking away the silk flowers they just plucked from your favorite arrangement that they are hanging onto with a death grip? To them it is very important to hold onto them for some reason. Let them keep it eventually they will find the perfect place to leave that silk rose, even if it is shoved into the flour canister.

In Home Care

This is the first step so many **people** take. Someone is hired to help a little at home, maybe some cooking, light housework, laundry this type of thing. A companion to go shopping or out to lunch with your person. Hire someone after putting your **Sherlock** on, doing some background and reference checks. As time goes on and the disease progresses you may have to extend the hours so someone can help with getting them up and dressed, provide their meals and help them get undressed and put in bed. As **mobility** decreases it will become time to make a change of where they live. Hiring help on your own can be costly. Check what is available through insurance. Research it, there is help out there.

Incontinence

You might be surprised to find out that most **people** who suffer with dementia are NOT incontinent. The difficulty comes when they go into the bathroom and do not know what to do. Going to the bathroom becomes an issue because the urge to go is there and just as urgent or **painful** as it can be for you or me. Imagine for a moment that you are in dire need to pee in a foreign country, you cannot read the signs, speak the language and no one is **understanding** you. Your biggest **fear** suddenly is that you will have an accident in front of everyone, would you become, short? Rushed? Angry? Try to hide? Perhaps even urinate somewhere inappropriate? (Men seem to find a dark hidden corner or even a house plant. Women tend to become upset and panic.) Something so private is now a public issue. Strangers even escort you into the restroom and must help with the intimate job of cleaning you up. Imagine the shame of having a 20-year-old girl or boy wiping your butt. Or your daughter, or wife.

Independent Living

The move to a community with other independent seniors. Friendship, **safety** and a space of their own. This is the first move to admitting it is time to downsize and enjoy your senior years. Ideally it is where they will live for the rest of their lives, knowing it is a scary possibility they will become a blubbering mass of confusion and be moved to the **assisted living** phase with **supervision** and then to a nursing home or locked **memory care** unit, to die. Granted not all of our loved ones end up in a nursing home, so **Sherlock**, do your homework and check out your options. People who move into a community often fair socially better in a **memory care** community later than those who come from living a solitary life alone. Communities are popping up everywhere to accommodate all those Baby Boomers and their needs.

Insomniac

The stress of taking care of your person will get extremely difficult if they become an insomniac. Working, managing a life with kids and caring for an elderly parent with dementia will drain you emotionally on its own, but throw insomnia into the mix and it is a train wreck. Remember how difficult it was to get your first grader dressed and out the door on time for the school bus? Well that was easy compared to trying to keep to a time schedule while caring for someone with dementia. Time has no meaning to them, nor do they care. Get some help. You cannot be everything for everyone. Overnight **caregivers** will give you the relief you will need, some badly needed sleep and some piece of mind to keep `your own sanity. If your person lives in a community perhaps they prefer the quiet found in the deep night time.

Integrity

Please feed your person's integrity. **Ask** their advice, talk about life and current events, feed their mind, even when it seems senseless to you because they can only answer you with **word salad**. They are answering and giving their opinion. Remind them of who they are, things they did and stood for in their lifetime, their accomplishments. Don't let them lose their integrity.

Intellectual Stimulation

The brain is a muscle and it can be worked. Help keep it working. As the disease process happens, you may need to **simplify** your topics.

*Dan is so angry with himself he was a teacher and is lost in that world where he can't even speak in a clear sentence and had lapsed into silence to hide the incorrectness of his vocabulary. He would linger on the outskirts of a group I was running. I **love** the intellectual programs we run. It is so fulfilling to see the way a topic can capture their attention and beautiful stories can pour out of those in the group. When it is an unusually tough group, and no one is participating, I can always count on **proverbs**, song lyrics or states and capitols to find success. "A rolling stone gathers no.." "Moss!" someone will finish for me. "You should never count your chickens before they.." "Hatch!" Dan muttered." "Awesome Dan I heard that!" I cheer him on. "What did he say?" One of the others demanded. "Hatch" I repeated with a big smile. "Make hay while.." " "The sun shines!" A couple **people** chime in, including Dan. I counter with "Red sky at night.." "Sailors delight." four or five call out. "Red sky in the morning.." "Sailors take warning!"*

even more call out joining the group of voices. Dan looks genuinely amazed as I smile at him. "How do I know all this?" he asks softly in disbelief. "Because you are brilliant" I say gently. "I don't know these." I need a cheat sheet with the answers!" I show them my pages from which I am reading. Everyone seems to brighten just a little bit, sit a little straighter in their chairs and **feel** a little stronger and more self-assured as we continue with the **exercise**. Success!

Intelligence

Admire it for your person as long as you can. Discuss their life's work. Tell your Dad that you are experiencing a funky noise in your car and **ask** what he might think it is, how do you fix a leaky faucet? **Ask** your Mom how she made that perfect pie, remove the ink stain, cook the perfect cookies. The answers do not matter at all! Just the fact that you asked and listened to their input, will make them **feel** valued. And you never know, at that moment they may be able to grasp the **correct** words to respond.

Interests

What are they? Just because someone was a seamstress for a living doesn't mean that they are interested in sewing in their dementia phase. Eyesight and dexterity can play a role in the disinterest. There are safe plastic needles and needle point canvases that can entertain an avid sewer. Or maybe arts and crafts are a favorite activity. Thumbing through magazines. Taking apart and putting together puzzles, model cars with big pieces, anything football? Cooking? Reading? Even if they cannot absorb the content. Put on your **Sherlock Holmes** Hat and do some investigating. Try new things, you will be surprised and when you find something that captures their interest you will **feel** successful!

Internet

In today's world who doesn't **love** the internet. This a great way to share **family** news via emails, make your person an email address and open it and read it with them they will be amazed. Show them your **family** photo's You can enlarge anything to make it easier for them to see and adjust the volume for them to hear. Try flying to their childhood home and let them see the old homestead today from the street view. Watch laughing babies, silly dogs and adorable kittens on you tube. Find Frank Sinatra crooning. Visit Paris, go to a museum. A wonderful tool to be used with **supervision** and help. If not supervised no telling where their searches and pop ups might take them. As social barriers cease to exist, and sexual interest never really goes away you may find out that unsavory sites are being visited.

Investigate

You will become your own private investigator, **Sherlock**. You will talk to neighbors, make keen observations, follow up on the stories and explanations your person gives. Please do not be a bulldozer as you do this. Don't be blatant, abrupt, accusatory, demanding. This will only insult your person and cause them to distrust you. Be clever and subtle. You will **feel** successful and you solve the mysteries your person presents. Share your insights with care givers and **family** members to help them with their interactions. Become **Sherlock Holmes.**

IPOD

If They will wear it and use headphones or earbuds awesome. If not a speaker will do just fine. Take time to download their favorite **music** and make play lists. Classical to relax, Bob Dylan and The Beatles to cheer them up. Barbara Streisand to **sing** along. Maybe they **love** country or big band. You get my drift. **Music** is magic.

Dan is unable to communicate without **word salad**. *He sits in his wheelchair and nothing seems to connect with him. His* **family** *brought in an* **IPOD** *loaded with the Blues greats he was unopposed to listening through the headphones. The volume had to be adjusted for his lack of hearing (there could be an issue if your person uses a hearing aid) and within a few minutes he began humming with his eyes closed as he drifted to some far-away place and time. After about 45 minutes and the* **head phones** *were removed and he chatted not stop with lit up eyes all through lunch. In complete relevant sentences. Amazing.*

It Doesn't Really Matter

Most of the time it really doesn't. Does your person pour milk on their cake and prefer it that way for desert? Do they eat their ice-cream with their fingers? Do they layer **clothing** that does not match when before the disease, they were a fashion diva? You decide. Are you taking on the challenge of correcting the situation because it is **dangerous** for them or is it because it bothers you. You must decide. Save your energy for the battles that really do matter.

J

Jealousy

You may encounter this in the oddest ways. It may manifest itself out of nothing in early stages. Things may turn up missing or get taken just because those moral barriers are dissolved. They may target you with jealousy because of your freedom, you can remember, you are the boss now. You could become the envied brother or sister, popular classmate or woman that perhaps her husband has flirted with. Just know it's real intense and very real to them, you can't downplay it.

Judgement

Your person will have **bad judgement** that is a given. Again, **ask** yourself is it just a little bad or **dangerous**. Are they giving away **money**? Do they eat uncooked meat? Are they washing dishes in the washing machine? Do they want to go shopping and buy odd things just because? Are they preparing wholesome meals or living on Oreo cookies and milk? Will they drink mouthwash because it **tastes** good? **Sherlock** you have your work cut out for you. If it is not **dangerous** or unhealthy, let them be. Take them to a yard sale for fun purchases. Bring in a housekeeper, let them help you cook and prepare meals under **supervision**.

Just Go With It

It doesn't make sense, but you have to just **go with it**. Read their expression, is it **laughter** and fun? **Anger** and **frustration**? **Fear** and anxiety? You will know the correct response when you can read their signs they are giving you. It will become easy to join them in their world and time. Just as they may respond to their given name better than Mom or Dad. You will have no idea what time frame they are living, although they will give you an idea. If they are talkative **ask** them how old they are. The answer just might surprise you, 20? 18? 12? 32?

Justify

You can forget trying to have your person justify any thing they have done or not done. That **reasoning** concept just won't exist.

K

Kindness

HUGE. Whatever you do, whatever you say, your tone of voice your **approach** do it with kindness. Remember always they cannot help it, it is the disease making them repeat **questions** for the thousandth time in a twenty minute period or every time you see them. Don't be frustrated if they **ask** you about your grades in college and thinking you are in school, when really you are headed for 60. It is the time frame they are in at that moment. You were very important to them at that time. They were hoping for the best for you and wanted you to have a successful future. They still do, so **just go with it**. Give the gift of kindness by not **correcting** them always.

Kisses and Hugs

Human needs. When we are young growing up hugs and kisses were a common need we all had for emotional growth. Your person is on a backwards roller coaster and they need the warmth of hugs and kisses to let them know they are not lost and alone. You have them covered so offer hugs and kisses. There is nothing more evident that when a person is under this disease their need for **love** intensifies. You may become their mother, father, husband, wife, secretary, cousin, lost **love** or best friend. The hugs and kisses become so necessary for them. **Go with it!**

L
Languages
Childhood language, French? Spanish? Hungarian? Your person may resort to speaking it again. Even if they have not spoken it since entering grade school. Those memories surface, they may be fluent or just an occasional word here and there. There are amazing apps that you can download and use it to record your person, or it will record you in English and translate to whatever language you choose. It is quite possible they **understand** English but will answer

Laughter
It is wonderful. Good for the soul. Hardly anything about this disease is laughable. It is downright depressing. Making your person laugh is powerful. Work on developing this talent and your person's journey will be all the better. I made it a personal goal when working in a **memory care** community of 64 residents to get as many smiles, laughs and **hugs** from my **people** as I could each day. That was my first and most important task for each resident as we danced their waltz.

Learned Behavior
Repetition. What our minds forget, our bodies remember. How to **shuffle** cards. You do not think, I reach for the cards, divide the pack in both hands so the piles are

equal. I hold them very carefully fingers pressing in the middle, lifting the corner closest to me with my thumb and slowly let the go folding into each other. then I push the two mixed piles into one, pick up the deck and do it again. 7 steps. Yet when you do it you just do it. You have not thought about the process of how you do it since you were eight years old and just learning. Your person may not be able to speak a whole sentence but they may be able to **shuffle** and deal a hand of poker. They may not be able to spell one word correctly but will set up the scrabble board and place misspelled **words** on the triple score squares just to beat you. They will **pray** and pour through a bible like they know it well.

Let It Go

Use your judgement, no telling what your person may tell you. You might be shocked or dismayed.

Molly was in a group and we were discussing first kisses. We all remember our first kiss. I asked each person who their first kiss was and would they share where and when it was. No one could remember so they said but all it took was myself confessing that my first kiss was my next-door neighbor under a weeping willow tree at the age of 13. I shared that I had had a crush on him for such a long time, with a giggle. That was all it took, stories began pouring out them. Molly remained quiet and I asked her directly if she wanted to share her story. She was frowning completely perplexed and said, "I don't know, I should know but I don't." I assured her not to worry it would come to her and continued with the others. When it was time for the group to end and head to the dining room for lunch suddenly Molly called out beaming "I remember! I remember my first kiss!" So, happy for her accomplishment I stopped dead in my tracks and said "That is awesome, I knew it would come to you. Who was it Molly?" With the biggest smile, ever she giggled like a schoolgirl and said "my brother!" I took a deep breath, smiled and said, "See I knew it would come back to you...Now it's time to head for lunch though, are you hungry? Will you have a cheese burger or the salmon?" I glossed over what could have been an embarrassing situation. Better to just let some things go.

Liquids

All are drinkable right. If you have dementia you might think so. Water from the flower vase, mouthwash, dish soap, shampoo perfume, hand sanitizer. The list goes on. If your person is trying to drink something **dangerous** it is just a sign that they are thirsty. Give them a cup of water or juice.

Listen

Always take the time to listen. If your person is sharing a story with you, give them your undivided attention as they **talk**, even if they are speaking a mix of **words** that make no sense at all. When I was very young I had an aunt that taught 1st and 2nd graders. She told me I should write to her and she would write back to me. Being a teacher she promised that she would **understand** every word I wrote. I bet I sent her 20 letters of nothing but scribbles thinking I was working on my penmanship. My mother bless her heart provided addressed envelopes and stamps for those very important letters. My aunt responded to everyone. She listened to my nonsense although I really thought I was being very articulate. Your person will think they are being very articulate, so please listen although every word is of the utmost **importance**. Encouragement goes a long way.

Look Around
Safety is your persons #1 need from now on. You need to be their protector and guide. It will be a gradual thing, you may just brush it off as getting forgetful. They may get lost driving or turn the wrong way headed home. They can't remember phone numbers that they've had memorized. They misplace bills. Put clean dishes in the fridge or dirty ones in the cupboard. Small little things.

Love
The good thing about love is that you always have more to give. We find this to be true when it comes to our **children** spouses, parents, and God. You will be tested as you dance with your person through the **dementia waltz**. Now is your chance to get to know the young businessman your father was, or the adventures he had as a **youth**. Your mom might **talk** about an old beau, or the **feelings** she had as a young woman. The first time they rode in a car, or drove a car. They might tell you the make and model. You can love who they used to be.

*Molly was very critical of everything but one of her favorite games was to look at black and white head shots of movie stars. She was very good at it, quite the movie buff. This particular day I held up the photo of Robert Mitchum and she leaned forward in her chair and said "he was my lover when I lived in New York. I was 24 years old." We were all speechless. I remarked how amazing that was, and was he a good man? We chatted about him for a while. I loved her **imagination**. Then later we were **talking** have you ever met anyone famous and she chirped in yes, Robert Mitchum. Same story they were lovers in NY for a couple months. I wonder, you just never can be sure.*

M

Magic Moment

You just never know when one will happen. When you have turned a bad moment back into a good one. Your person is bursting with pride a completing a task. They look you in the eye and say I **love** you. You came into the community and saw your mom giggling like a schoolgirl with the other ladies. Your Dad introduces you to a new friend. He is pleased to let you know they used to work together over 40 years ago! Magic. **Pray.** This is a perfect time to do so, thanking God for your success and for the chance to see your person through this, and for helping you make their dance through the **dementia waltz** as enriching as possible.

Mean

The sweetest kindest person can show their inner **meanness**. It is so hard on **family** and friends when their person has a complete personality reversal. It kind of makes you wonder if exorcisms work. I have heard cussing pour out of the mouth of a woman who never swore in her life. **Anger** and **fury** become the emotion best shown. Again please don't blame them, sympathize instead.

Medications

Medication or medications may be used to minimize the effects of certain kinds of dementia, for a limited amount of time. Not a Cure. If you have a cold and take medicine for aches and **pains**, it helps the symptoms for 4 hours. You still have a cold.

Medicine Taking

Gross and disgusting especially if it has to be crushed. Much like a rebellious teenager they will defiantly refuse. Or maybe like an angry toddler just shut their mouth and refuse passage or the ever stressful spit it out. Can you blame them? Not only does it **taste** absolutely disgusting, but you are not listening to them and the fact that they just don't want to. Try hiding it in something flavorful that they like, pudding, yogurt, ice-cream, apple sauce. This makes it slippery as well to help with swallowing. Try not to use the same one all the time it never takes long to catch on. It might help too to offer something else after to help remove the **taste**, a cookie, or just more medicine free ice-cream might work. **Quality not Quantity**.

Memory Care

A softer kinder name than dementia care. The families prefer it and the residents that live in a locked down community respond better to hearing memory care facility. They may even join in on all programs offered believing their memory might actually improve.

Memory Impairment

Just that. The memories are missing, misplaced, lost, impaired. Not on **purpose**. As time goes on more and more memories will disappear. A gentle way of not saying Dementia.

Mirror

Does your person look at their reflection and not know who that old person is looking back at them? To a person with dementia this is an unrecognizable old person looking in a window. I have worked in communities where the mirrors need to be removed. Because of this real **fear**, help them live without mirrors.

Mobility

You will hear this word often, simply put, it just speaks about how well your person moves about. Are they totally independent, need some assistance with a cane, walker or wheelchair? Do they **fall**, how unsteady on their feet are they?

Money

Someone will have to handle your persons money. This would be the financial **Power of Attorney** (POA). Not to be confused with Medical **Power of Attorney** (POA). That person makes all the medical **decisions**. I have worked in communities where cash on hand, in wallets can cause serious problems. It may get lost, taken or get hidden. The best part is that if another resident takes it they are in a lockdown community and it doesn't go far. Better to not put your person or anyone else in that position. If they need cash lock it up in a safe place until needed.

Morale

Important to keep morale up, your own and your persons. Do cheerful things together, **Music**? Go to a concert or **musical** even if they can't stay for the whole production. Celebrate birthdays, holidays, **talk** on the phone. Check in with them like they matter.

Mourn

The person you **love** is morphing into someone else, a younger more vulnerable version of themselves. It is perfectly ok to mourn the mom, dad, husband or wife you have lost. It can be a long journey with years of **sadness** and decline. Someone once said, "Without change there would be no butterflies," mourn the caterpillar, **love** the **butterfly**.

Movement

Keep them **moving**. As much as you can **exercise** will tire them out, and make their **pains** ease a little. Remember the old proverb, "If you don't use it you will lose it."

Moving

The decision to move your person is huge and traumatic no matter how necessary. This will be an undertaking that will **feel** enormous. Not only do have to convince your person it is for the best but you have the overwhelming task of down sizing and cleaning out a lifetime collection of stuff. Taking what they need is first, then what they want and they will most likely want it all. Going through it all, cookbooks, furniture, knickknacks, tools, **clothing**, jewelry. What do you do with the car? The collection of tea cups? The pictures? **Breathe.** 10x slowly. Incorporate **family** to help you. Hopefully you do not have to take on this endeavor all alone.

Muscle Memory

You always remember how to ride a bike, they say. That is if you ever rode one. Your muscles remember, you do it without thinking. How to walk upstairs, you lift your leg and place your foot, muscle memory. At the dentist, your person reclines they clip a splatter guard around your neck and they open their mouth wide, muscle memory. If they took good care of their teeth and went to a dentist regularly they may still remember the routine. The knitter might be able to knit even when **word salad** has taken over.

Music

Pure Magic! Embrace the gift to all of us that music is. From infancy we have learned that music is the universal **language**. The variety of musical options out there are limitless. Put on your **Sherlock** hat and find what music your person loves, or did **love**. Not your choice, theirs. The oldies to them are current and fresh. **Why** do some songs make them **cry** others joyful and yet others dance. Classical jazz, country, rock, strings, harp, big band, folk, bluegrass, country, salsa, jazz, Motown? **Love** songs concertos? Piano, guitar, strings, choir, soloists? You get it. This a great way to guide you person to a good experience. It's so simple use your **common sense**. Play up beat music for **exercise** or while doing busy tasks. Use soft and soothing during sun-downing times. Your person just loved Bob Dylan? Put him on if some soothing needs to happen. We all **love** music that takes us places, that will never change. If **music** is not available, then just **hum** or **sing**.

N

Napping

Good for the soul. I recommend that you just let it happen. **Medications** and physical **exercise** even just walking can be cause to take a nap. As we age we **sleep** more. You too should consider taking one every now and then. It will refresh you.

Needed

We all have a **desire** to feel needed. Whether it is by our families, work or friends, it makes us **feel** good to **feel** needed, wanted, valued. Your person still feels this way too but their world is getting smaller and they may be feeling like a burden, not needed and valued.

News and Newspapers

Watching the news used to be the routine after dinner for all American families. Reading the paper at breakfast was normal. This can easily be avoided. Due to the content of news today I highly recommend that you move into a game show or comedy instead. Your person may not be able to decipher between **TV** and **reality**. A crime show may cause a real **fear**, a zombie can haunt them in the night time, a war movie may send him right back to Vietnam. Try an old Western or a comedy instead.

No Pain

I have met a few people who seem to feel no pain. I mean no pain at all.

*Dan a resident I knew had **fallen** and **needed** to go to the hospital for stitches was all I was told. It was my job to keep him company and not let him **escape** or wander off until he was done and be his ride back. I got my car ready and here he came with his thumb wrapped up. The care giver told me they did know how it happened but he had opened up his thumb and the bone was exposed. I was not ready* *for a good natured rambunctious man who was insisting that his cut thumb was nothing and he was quickly unwrapping it. In emergency he was charming and flirtatious to the attending, and bantered with the doctor the whole time insisting his thumb was fine. He would poke it and pull the hanging part, and grabbing the bone. I think even the Doctor was shocked. He decided to clean and stitch it right away, applying the numbing injections. Dan was giving in to him working on it. He just shook his head and let them sew him up insisting the whole time that this was kind of them but totally unnecessary. This can be a serious part of dementia, it can be very* **dangerous***. Did he feel no pain? Who knows?*

Now Go With It

You are in it now, so **breathe** 10x's in through your nose, out through your mouth and then just go with it.

Dan is captivated by the flower arrangement on the dining room table. He is plucking the stems out one by one. I attempt to remove the bouquet and he grabs it back with a vengeance. I give in and just go with it. I watch and openly admire each flowers color as the get removed and occasionally he tells me their name. "daisy". He plucks out a Mum and says "rose". When they are all laid out on the table he re adjusts a couple to line them up in corresponding colors. Finished he walks away from the table. I admire his work and salvage what I can, enjoying the task of rearranging them. I wipe the table dry and realize no harm done, the arrangement looks good but most importantly Dan finished his task, was satisfied with his work and moved on.

We started to tango but ended with a sweet waltz.

Nurturing

Everyone needs to be nurtured. **Encouraged** and loved tenderly. We all have the option as we grow up to become a nurturer. It is quite easy once you get used to it. Be positive, and look on the bright side of everything. **Talk** about the beauty of the sky and clouds. The colors of the leaves in the Autumn. Let them help you bake cookies. Play cards even though they have forgotten the rules, and they always win. Feed their soul.

*It was summertime and Molly always had her seat at the same table every day. She would have her black coffee and chat with the aids. We had planted the spring flowers and tied a scarecrow on the 6 foot cast iron fence that enclosed the patio (**safety**). He was behind a hedge and resembled a person of average height. He was missing his hat so we had replaced it with a red baseball cap. "There he is!" She announced to everyone. "There's that man, he is standing right in the sunshine." I came over beside her and looked, sure enough she was talking about the scarecrow. He became her focus so much that I changed his clothes to a coat, scarf and winter hat. "I don't know **why** he wants to stand there in the snow" Molly would shake her head. "He is my friend" We nurtured her heart.*

O
Offensive Behavior

Social skills become non-existent. Remember this.

*Dan went out for lunch with his **family** to a popular pizza restaurant. They sat on the side of the large dining area hoping the noise from the other diners would not be over-stimulating. After their order was taken Dan announces that there are no coloreds at his place. He is looking around the room at the mixture of many races that are dining on pizza at that moment. "Well actually we did for a while but she just served us our meals. She didn't last long. It's not like this place!" Dan's son, daughter-in-law, and grandchildren are horrified. **People** are looking at them with no **understanding** of Dan's dementia. He is*

*just a rude uncouth old man. Network your conversations, so Dan's son
says, "That's right dad, how many* **people** *do you think live at your
place?" He moved the* **conversation** *into a different* **direction** *and
the other customers went back to their meal, still insulted.*

Outrageous Behavior

Yes, it is bound to happen. Imagine how shocked you
would be if your sweet gentle mother decided to disrobe in
the dining room in front of the other residents and fought off
anyone trying to stop her.. How difficult would it be to see
your kind, gentle father furiously ripping apart his bed and
emptying his dresser drawers with a vengeance looking for
something only he knows what it is. What if they go after
another resident and hit them? No one knows **why** or cares,
what is important is to sooth them and ignore the behavior
while trying to change it.

P

Pacing

Some people pace back and forth, back and forth a
repetitive pattern. Others just have to be doing something so
they walk, and walk and walk. You will have no idea **why** or
what they are looking for but **It doesn't really matter.** If
your person lives at home, you have the **fear** of them
becoming lost, if you have them living in a community there
is staff trained for this behavior.

*Dan had to walk constantly. He would walk until exhaustion made
him stumble and clip doorways with his shoulder. I would always invite
him to sit down in a chair or on a couch. It was my belief that it was*
painful *to bend and sit so I would guide him into his seat. "Boy Dan I
think you walked 20 miles this morning. Can I get you something cold*

68

to drink? You must be thirsty!" I always push the fluids because he cannot find his **words** to **ask**. I bring him some juice and he gulps it greedily. I **wait** till he is done and offer more. When finished he immediately leaves, continuing on his journey. Remember dehydration is a **dangerous** risk to those with dementia.

Pain

Put on your **Sherlock**. If your person is verbally challenged and in pain how will they tell you? They cannot say "Hey I have a head ache! Keep the noise down." But they can seek out a quiet place to sit, and hold his head, rub his temples and hide his head under a pillow. They can't tell you they have a tooth ache. Be their voice.

Patience

Find it. Use it. Your person will test your patience like it has never been tested before. You be asked the same question over and over. You will be cleaning constantly behind your person, but you have to remember you can't blame them. They do not mean it, it is the disease process. **Breathe**, take a break, walk away count to ten. Do whatever works for you. But find patience then try a new **approach**.

People

There will be times your person may **fear** everyone. Even **family** members. There may be times your person loves every one and rushes up to strangers, gushing in **word salad** to a startled stranger. Your **business card** may come in very handy.

Personal Hygiene

This could be one of the telltale signs that your person is suffering from some form of dementia. Unruly hair, dirty unkempt **clothing**, body odor, teeth that need brushing. When a person if fighting the beginning to mid stage dementia, the feeling that something is wrong gnaws at them. Even though they cannot and will not voice the feeling something is wrong and not within their control, they cover it up. You and I would do the same, to buy time until we can **fix it**. Trouble is they won't be able to **fix it**.

Pick Your Battles

Save your energy for the ones that matter.

Play an Instrument

It is **music**! Pull out your old guitar, harmonica or trumpet. Practice and fool around with it, your person will be appreciative. Guaranteed. If they played an instrument they may still be able to. Try it.

Play the Radio

Turn it on.

Possessive

Your person can become very fixated on you, a **caregiver** or items. This is not really a bad thing unless it becomes **dangerous** refusing to let go or put down a glass figurine for instance. You can use this fixation to calm, soothe to **talk** and discuss. To **validate**.

Post-traumatic Stress Disorder

A whole different ball game. Throwing dementia into the mix of flash backs and you have an explosive situation. Contact the closest VA for more information and help.

Power of Attorney

It will be hard to realize that someone else makes all your **decisions** for you, whether you disagree or not. When your person hands over POA and medical POA it was a very wise and rational decision. You were given the power because your person loves, trusts and counts on you to do what is right.

The power can bite you, hard. Everything becomes your fault and it is a heartbreaking cross to bear. Here is the parent that raised and protected you, seething with **anger** because you will not bring them home. The look in his eye chills you to the bone and breaks your heart in pieces. At this moment, everything in life that has gone wrong is blamed on you. Not the disease, not the doctor, not the care staff. Just you. You don't care, you don't **listen**, you only want their **money**. They may blame you.

Pray

For your person, for yourself as you dance through the disease process, for a cure. This journey will be challenging and overwhelming. You need to take care of yourself and allow yourself some reprieve. Pray with your person, they need comfort and **love** more than anyone you know. If they had any religious background in their **youth**, even if they lost it as an older adult, they will find comfort and remember the power of prayer. They will bow their head and **feel** the comfort that prayer can bring.

Dan was never very religious as an adult. He would wander into and out of the various programs offered at his community. When the different **church** *communities would bring services to the interested residents Dan would join the groups sitting through the messages, bowing his head in prayer,* **sing** *with the* **music** *and even quoting the Lord's Prayer.*

His **family** *was surprised to hear this since he never really attended* **Church** *that they recall. The comfort is that even through this disease process we all have the need to know God, to be* **forgiven** *to* **feel** *safe and loved. Dan's* **family** *welcomed the news of Dan's attendance to these programs. Participation in any programs makes them* **feel** *good, knowing Dan is* **engaged**. *This opens an unknown avenue for them to venture onto. They can now pray with Dan, a closeness that they have been searching for.*

Pressure Points

Sitting, laying, lack of **movement** will make a pressure point happen causing skin breakdown. As the muscles and skin become weaker and thinner leaning, sitting or laying in the same position for long periods of time make for a tender sore spot where the bone presses against the skin. These spots can open into an ulceration that can be deep and very difficult to heal.

Problem Solved

The pay off. When you can fix your person's anxiety, **sadness** or **frustration** it is a beautiful thing. Problem Solved.

Proverbs

I always called this, "The Things Your Mother Said a Million Times."

A rolling stone gathers no................(moss).
You can lead a horse to water but you can't.....(make him drink).
A bird in the hand is worth 2 in the...................(bush).
You should never put all your eggs in one.........(basket).
A leopard can't change its ....(spots).
Don't count your chickens before they...................(hatch).
Never look a gift horse in ....(the mouth).
Look them up. Bring them with you when you go to visit. This they will know or seem to recall when you read them out loud. Pause before finishing and let them fill in the blanks. They may always be right but their wrong answers can be fun too, or if they are wrong, tell a **fiblet** that they are exactly right. Pump up their ego!

Purpose

We have to have purpose to feel **needed**, alive and to be wanted. Everyone. As long as you have something to contribute to anyone or anything you have purpose. Do not let your person feel like a burden. Give them purpose. Tell them what you thinking, doing or want to do. **Ask** for their advice, give them **direction** and let them feel valued.

Q
Quality not Quantity

Allowing your person (now that you are 100% their decision maker /care giver) to have the best quality of life (however long) verses a very long unfulfilled life. Simple, scary and always challenging, not stagnate, boring and useless. They are overweight but want ice cream. Let them have it. They insist on feeding themselves but make a terrible mess.

Let them. They want to walk but their **mobility** is terrible, a **fall** risk for sure. Grab a care-giver and walk with him. Give him that **dignity**.

Questions

So many, unanswered for you. So many from your person over and over. They can tire you out and frustrate you like you have never been frustrated before. The beauty of it is that they just need some answers so tell them what they need to hear. We were brought up to always be honest to our parents, so the idea of **fiblets** may be out of your realm of comfort at first. The payoff is when your **fiblet** has soothed and calmed your person. It will become easier.

Quiet Time

Everyone benefits from quiet time every now and then. **Sun downing** time is a great time to do something easy and soothing for your person. A nap, a favorite **tv** show, **music**, reading (when they can't, read to them. The tone of your voice could lull them to a quiet place. Book on tape is good too.)

In the afternoon, I would deliberately read to my residents. I chose "Go set a watchman" by Harper Lee. Everyone had read or seen To Kill a Mocking Bird and I used that to my advantage. Before reading I we **reminisced** about the movie with Gregory Peck. All the Ladies recalled him easily. I had pulled his photo up on the **internet** and showed it to the group. Visual **cueing**. I would remind them of what we had previously read, before beginning. I would announce several times throughout the day that we were reading more later that afternoon.

*Molly loved books and wrote little bits of wisdom on any piece of paper she could find. She recorded every thought and memory with a passion. She would pour through books and magazines, and was known to rip a page or two or three out to share with a staff or **family** member. She was my inspiration to begin the book club. Molly who usually napped a good part of the afternoon let it be known to everyone she saw that she needed to be up for the book reading. She would sit next to me for every reading and with happiness and excitement she would laugh chuckle and pat my arm as we followed Scout through her grown-up years. Her delight was obvious. With reading out-loud on a soothing voice You can bring your person into a quiet time when **sun-downing** is a real risk.*

R

Reality

What is reality anyway? Yours, mine, theirs? Their reality will be ever changing. The ability for them to **understand** your reality will diminish. The reality is whatever place in time they happen to be living in at that moment. They may be looking for their Mom or Dad, they may be a **flirty** young adult with their focus being one of the care staff or the building maintenance guy, or they are looking for their baby and need to get home!

Dan, living in a memory care facility, told me that as soon as this cruise ship docked he had to get home and back to work. His reality.

Reasoning

If this is your Strategy, **let it go**. As much as your person will want to make you happy, they will not be able to follow your reasoning. Yours is not to question **why**, **just go with it**. You can reason **why** out loud with your person and discuss any idea you are thinking about. They will **listen** intently and respond. The good thing is they won't tell anyone.

Red Flags

That little voice in your head that nags at you. Feeling confused after a **conversation**, seeing something that isn't quite right. Doubt.

Redirect

Your best bet. Always. This simple technique once developed will save your sanity. Once mastered beware of using it on everyone! Use any means nearby.

*Molly is trying the locked front door, headed out to get the **children** from school. You are her 50 year old child but she just thinks you are crazy calling her Mom. Her children are in school and you are old. Call her by her name and point something out with enthusiasm and excitement. "Molly! Would you look at this picture! Is this your fathers house?" She will look at the picture, glancing away from the door. "No!" she turns back and rattles the handle." What did his house look like? Are you sure this isn't it Molly?" Molly walks toward you and shakes her head no. But she is now standing with you looking at the painting. You have redirected.*

*Dan is trying to change the channel with his remote but has pushed many buttons losing connection. His **frustration** is growing and bad **language** right along with it. He will not give you the remote either. Turn the TV off manually. Pop in a cd of his favorite songs to **sing** along to. Just burst out to "Take me out to the Ball Game." The **music** will captive his attention and now turning off the television manually may need to happen and he will give up the remote. Or maybe not but that's ok too. You **sing** along, it could be a lot of fun.*

Reminisce

This works all the time. Remember when. What was your wedding like. Did you ever own a dog? What color was he? Was he big?

Who was your favorite teacher in school? What was so nice about her? Was she pretty?

How did you and dad meet? Was it **love** at first sight? Did he chase you or did you chase him?

Tell me about Christmas, what do you like best about it? Shopping for gifts? The **food**? Do you like real trees or did you have an artificial one? Do you **love** to ride around and look at the lights in the neighborhoods? Did you decorate the outside of your house?

See what I mean? It becomes easy to do, the more you **ask** the more you will know and the more you will have to reminisce about. This is called Quilting, as you piece the **conversation** into a **direction** that is enjoyable for your person. Just avoid **Why**. "**Why** did you move"? They won't know **why**.

Repetition

Over and over again. **Words, questions, movements**. It will happen because your person is working for the solution to what, they are not sure but they have to keep looking. It is human nature. If they keep **moving**, they might find it. The answer might come to them. Doing something is better than doing nothing at all.

Repetitive Movements

Hands banging, tapping, rubbing, pinching. The constant **movement** that can happen to some. Repetitive **words** and chanting also happens. It depends on what parts of the brain are affected and being devoured by the disease. Grinding teeth falls in with repetitive movement. They cannot help it.

Resources

Check all the resources you can. Groups, books, search on line, make calls, **ask**. Use them. Find medical answers, management techniques, caring & sharing, **ask** staff in communities for recommendations. Read and search the **internet** for it! Watch others with how they handle their **people**. **Talk** about it.

Respect

Always respect your person. Your **approach** must be with respect no matter how difficult this can be. If you want the dance to be a smooth waltz verses a miss-stepped jive, always treat your person with respect. **Ask** their permission, opinion, thoughts. Even when you have to answer for them, still **ask** with respect, and respond with respect. Explain things, show things reach their inner **dignity** that we have.

Routines

Rather important to a few, very important to others but an absolute must for some. Up at regular time, meals being served at the same time, dressing for bed and washing up might ensure your person **sleeps** soundly and hopefully won't wander at night. So much comes into play with this scheduling feat. First put your **Sherlock** on and find out what the current schedule is for your person. Try to follow it as closely as possible. If your person is **moving** in with you, you will want a routine, trust me. If you have to **hire help** to make it happen, do it. A calm routine will minimize outbursts of rough **behaviors**.

S

Sadness

Maybe the most heart breaking mood of all. It is mellow and long lasting. You might be able to bring bits of happiness to your person, but some sadness may linger. Your person has to deal with the **reality** that they have lost their independence, house, **family**, friends, pets and are losing their memories. This disease is taking their life away. That **reality** brings sadness, and until they find their place in their new community it will linger, and that takes time. For some sadness just won't ever let go.

Safety

The most important thing you can do for your person is to look out for their safety. Let your Mother/Father bear come out. Your life has never been so all consuming with one focus like it has now. You will suddenly realize everything you own is **dangerous** to a person with dementia. Safety will become your first priority. Are the locks foolproof, is medication being taken correctly? Are the **shoes** a good sturdy fit? Is there scatter rugs that might be a trip hazard? Are knives too **dangerous** to leave out and can become a weapon? Scissors? Nail Clippers? Will they eat the flowers? Are the house plants poisonous? Do they wander and get lost? Will they put that in their mouth and try to eat it and choke? Could they use that as a weapon? You get my drift. Safety.

Sexual Inhibitions

The last thing you want to experience from a parent or spouse. The heartbreak and turmoil you may face if this is an emotion your person acts out on without barriers. It does happen. Be prepared to think out of the box.

Dan had a tendency to disrobe. He just fought every minute to take his clothes off. It did not matter to him who was witnessing the act of disrobing, or where he was. His dementia had progressed to the point where he could not explain his need for his clothes to be gone. Is it the texture? The feeling of seams or tags? Staff chased him constantly coaxing him to put that shirt on again or change those slacks to shorts in case he was too hot. This however was not his solution, everything still came off. His wife with a lot of thought and searching found adult onesies. He looked like he had 2 pieces of **clothing** *on but they were sewn together and it had a zipper in the back, out of his reach. Tug as he might he could not disrobe and eventually would give up.*

Sherlock Holmes

Be your own sleuth. You have to read the whole picture to find the clues and solve the problem at hand. Sometimes the answer you are looking for is very obvious.

Mary always loved to see me when I came in to work. She was a tall sturdy woman, who used her walker with a fierce intensity as she clipped a good pace all day back and forth throughout the community. Her head would be down as she studied the path in front of her. I had a hunch she knew everyone's **shoes.** *She was always on a mission. When I would "bump" into her she would stop abruptly and give me a big smile and* **wait** *for my "Good Morning Sunshine!" and I would step up for a big hug or a kiss on the cheek whatever she was offering up that day. I recall* *the day I wore a red sheer blouse over a tank top and when I saw Mary headed my way I got ready for our ritual. Mary stopped and the seething angry look she gave me would have stopped a grown man in his tracks. She sneered and said "Yeah you think you're really something in that red smug don't you." Glared and took off down the hall. I was stunned. The Sherlock in me knew instantly that red blouse (smug) was not going to be worn again. It can be obvious. If you are lucky.*

Shoes
Sturdy and consider slip on or Velcro. Walking or their **Gait** will become an issue so stability is a must. Tying shoes may become an issue so do not set them up for failure.

Shoppers
The joy of it! Most **people** like to shop whether for others or themselves. Your person may enjoy it to a whole new level. Remember barriers no longer exist so things may get taken, stolen hidden, hoarded flushed (yes flushed) so keep your **Sherlock** on and watch. Most of the time it is just that she or he just will gather and collect or hide, so frequent clean outs when they are occupied so as to have no interference will usually work fine.

Molly was a walker and walked the halls of our community constantly. She had been a very physically active outdoorsman, kayaking, hiking, skiing. She was thrifty and loved a bargain. Yard sales were her favorite things to do on the weekends. She carried sale flyers around and share the wonderful deals she found usually on soda products. She would walk right into others rooms and look over their belongings and help herself to anything she liked. The community itself was her yard sale, and her newfound treasures would be carefully hidden or tucked away in the bottom of her closet. She would help herself to the snacks at the snack stations and for some reason would flush them down the toilet still in the wrappers. Believe me we found out the hard way, when we had to have the plumber come out pump out the mess.

Short Term Memory

Yesterday? An hour ago? Last week? **Why** is it your person can remember with clarity what they ate at the fair 20 years ago but can't tell you what they ate 10 minutes ago for lunch. The disease attacks short term memories first.

Shuffle

The way the strongest hiker or runner will also begin to walk.

Simplify

Two options, two choices. From **food** to **clothing** to channels to watch on TV, try to make it easy for them. A restaurant menu may overwhelm, an ice cream shop could be upsetting with all the choices. The simpler you make it for them, the better experience you both will have.

Sing

Need I say more? It works. Your person will not judge you if you try.

Singers

He who cannot speak may be able to **sing**.

Dan was aware his daughter was getting married. He wanted so badly to express how much he loved her, was happy for her, how he had waited for this moment this day her whole life. His dementia had not affected his motor skills yet so he was going to give her away. With sheer

determination *he wrote a poem. It was short and choppy but it expressed his* **love** *for his "girl" and the happiness he wished for the woman she had become. The magic of* **music** *let him* **sing** *his old favorite country songs word for word, for the most part. At the birthday celebrations he could* **sing** *each word loudly and clearly. He wanted so badly to speak the* **words** *he had written at her wedding. It was at the reception dinner he stood with the poem in hand and sang every word in his own voice to the tune of happy birthday to you. Singing uses a different part of the brain than speech.*

Music is magic. Keep **music** in your persons life and bring them to concerts, **play the radio**, invite anyone you know who loves to **sing** to go to the community where your loved one lives to entertain them.

Skilled Nursing Care

When your loved one needs 24 hour nursing care. Not just a friend or **caregiver** but a licensed Nurse. **Mobility** and **medications** will be key factors for this decision. **ADL's.**

Sleep

Sleep deprivation is a form of torture. We all need sleep. **Ask** for help, relief. Hire a **caregiver**, give the responsibility of over-seeing your person to the staff in a community. Get your rest so you can be the best you can be, rested and ready to waltz. Lack of sleep does terrible things to our bodies and mind. Do what you need to to assure yourself and your person that things are okay so you can both get enough sound sleep. As we age we do nod off and take naps. This is a normal need. Naps can be wonderful for the both of you.

Still Going With It?

I hope so. Just **Breathe** and go with the flow. The more you fight it the harder it will be on you. Keep it simple for your own sanity.

Still There

Never ever think your person is gone. They are still there, just in a different place and time. So find them wherever they are. **Just go with it.**

Molly was in an exceptionally good mood that morning, and welcomed me with a giggle and a "Guess What!" I had to giggle back and whispered "What?" She beamed up at me from her wheelchair and said "I am getting married today!"

*I just grinned and asked "who are you going to marry? Do I know him?" She nodded vigorously. "I'll show you!" she promised searching the common area where other residents were gathering for breakfast. I was curious which lucky gentlemen would be chosen as the lucky groom. She was so happy I just played along. "Do you see him yet Molly?" I inquired a few minutes later. I was walking by her spot where she was still looking around. "No, no....**wait, wait** a minute!" the excitement in her voice was contagious half the room turned to look down the hall that Molly was focused on. I too took a couple of steps back to see who it was making an entrance. I was running through my head the possibilities of that roomed down that particular hallway. I saw Jim, our 27 year old quite handsome man from Plant Operations. He had a ladder poised on his shoulder and beamed a beautiful smile at the group that was grinning at him. "Well, good morning everybody. What's going on?" he asked coming to a stop. "Its him! Its Him!" Molly exclaimed with such **love**. Jim just smiled down at her and said, "What do you **mean**, Molly?" he shot me a questioning glance. Molly just blushed a beautiful pink so I stepped in and said, "Well, my goodness, Jim, Molly just told us that she* was getting married today and that you are her groom." I **love** Jim's work ethic and the **love** and **respect** he has for all the residents. He just hesitated for the quickest second and then stood so proudly, puffed out his chest and said 'That's right and I am the luckiest guy. Oh, Molly I am not supposed to see you before the ceremony!!" He put the small ladder up against the wall, bent over, kissed Molly's cheek and said "I will see you later" picked up the ladder and continued on his way.

Molly's daughter came in shortly after and I had a chance to tell her what had transpired earlier. Jenny thought it was very funny, admitting she admired her mom's **taste** in men. When she approached her mom, she called her Molly, not mom, accepting that her mother was living in a time she couldn't possibly have a daughter her age! So the daughter had become the friend. Jenny was taking her mom for a stroll through the community discussing the many focal points that were strategically placed to **encourage** conversations. Molly took a large bouquet of flowers from a table. Molly shook her head. "No, no, no. Its not like before," she leaned closer to her daughter adding with a whisper " I will put these back. I had to throw the lilacs away, we stole them, you did it!!" Jenny, just going with it smiled and said "OK, we will pick them up on our way back from the walk, they look quite heavy." Molly nodded with some reluctance as Jenny began pushing her wheelchair. "Okay, but I'm getting married today!" Jenny wondered instantly if the lilacs that she clearly recalled that had adorned every pew and made a beautiful wedding bouquet in all her mom's wedding pictures had been stolen from neighbors by her mom and a friend. A hidden memory? You never know what you might discover. "Wait!" Molly said to Jenny looking at the arrangement. "I need those flowers! I have to have them just take them!" Molly ordered her daughter. "Molly, I can't just take these now. If we leave them just for a few minutes we can finish our walk and pick them up on the way back. That way they will last longer," Jenny suggests hoping when they come back the flowers will be forgotten.

Stubbornness

You can lead a horse to water but you can't make him drink. When your person digs their heels in there may be no persuasion that works. Let that issue whatever it is go, give in. Let them win, then very casually distract them onto a different topic.

Sun Downing

This is that dreaded part of the day when anxieties rise. It is that period of time when it is time to go. There are kids to pick up, groceries to buy, dinner to cook, friends coming for dinner, Parents will be angry they have got to go. The urgency to go home is unbearably intense sometimes and you are the prison guard keeping them from that mission. You don't even know what home they are **talking** about because they are at home! So **ask**, what does your house look like? Is it big? Try to distract them and **redirect** their attention.

*Molly lived in a community where the activities room had a wall of windows facing an elementary school. During the day some of the ladies loved to watch the **children** out on the playground. Let the buses pull up to take them home and chaos would ensue. " I have to go, I have to get dinner, There's no one home. The **Children** can't be alone. My mother will be mad. I want my dad." We very quickly learned that closing all the blinds helped and doing a **musical** activity helped sooth everyone until it was time to eat.*

Supervision

How much is too much, how little is not enough. How do you do it without seeming or feeling like a micro-manager? Can you check in once a week? Take them grocery shopping? Help write out the bills? Call them every evening to be sure that they are home and remind them to lock all the doors? Put on your **Sherlock**, but remember no one likes a bully.

Swearing

Remember, no barriers so that goes for the **language** your person may choose to say. Chances are they don't mean to, it just comes out. Show no reaction because in their mind the **words** are entirely different or like a kid they may think that's funny. Meaning of the **words** don't exist. Some swear continuously and this can cause isolation because it causes embarrassment.

T

Talk

Keep the **conversation** going, **ask** simple **questions**, **Either/Or**. Them, how your day was, **ask** how theirs was, tell a funny story that happened today, talk about that cute baby you saw. The more positive and good you talk about you will find they follow the lead. Their mood will lighten. Give them you're your undivided attention when they offer up a long-winded version of **word salad**, because there is some truth and sense in there if you **listen** very carefully. Keep them talking and talk back!

Task Oriented

Love to be of use. Keep them busy with simple tasks. They will give it some effort and what they end up with most likely will be far from perfect. For instance, folding towels or dusting. They may not fold anything the way you like it, or something could get broken when they tried to dust under it. It isn't the end result that is important. It is the journey. Keep them **feeling validated**. Let them feel **needed** and accomplished. Compliment them for helping, "Thank you so much for doing that for me." "I couldn't have done this without your help, Thanks."

Taste

Food is the one social event that keeps its **importance** until the end. **Food** is something that everyone always looks forward to and sweet are the last taste buds to go for most. Molly sometimes needed her mashed potatoes dipped in sugar to entice her taste buds. Ice cream or pudding is always welcome.

Tears

Wipe them or kiss them away. Something is wrong so comfort them through it until you figure out the fix.

Tell Stories

Talk about your day, keep them **listening** and involved. Tell stories about them, they like learning about themselves, what they've done. What they've accomplished, what they liked.

Tenderness

Find it and always and use it. Treat your person with tenderness.

Textures

Touch, **touching**, being touched. So very important Keeping hands busy keeps them grounded, it is real. There will also be textures that they no longer like. This might cause things to get thrown away or hidden. Use this as a chance to entice them into an engaging activity. **Ask** them to help you out and give them a basket or box of things to sort for you. Anything that captures their interest and is safe is great. Sort magazines, tools, **clothing**, the junk drawer. Use your **imagination**.

They Can't Help It

Dan loved to gravitate toward a small group of women, the same 4 or 5 every afternoon. He was very tall, and practically non-verbal. The **medications** *he was on cause him drool incessantly. The ladies had become very aware of this change and it scared them to see this 6 foot plus man making a beeline toward them, grinning from ear to ear, with drool dripping from his chin. He would lean over the fussing women and inadvertently slime one or two in close proximity. The closer he would get to them the more the angry outbursts from them would be heard down the hall. "Go away! Get out! Leave us alone! Stop! Get out of here you big lug!" Not to mention a few cuss* **words** *might follow. He would grin from ear to ear and just laugh, letting a little extra drool go. As a caregiver, I would* **approach** *very slowly with tissues in hand and* **ask** *him "Dan what are you doing? Teasing these girls?" I would* **ask** *offering tissues to those drooled upon, or wiping up the spit as I was speaking. I also would edge my way into his line of vision pulling his focus onto myself. "Can you come give me a hand for a minute Dan?" I would* **ask** *making the ever-important* **eye contact** *and smiling at him, ignoring the chorus of name calling and urgent requests to "take him away" I wiped his mouth again, handed him the tissue and tugged at his hand until he began to follow me. "It won't take a minute, I promise but I sure could use your muscle!" I gradually made my way to the bookcase down the hall where we took a moment to straighten up the books. A co-worker came by and said "Was he picking on those ladies*

89

again? He does it on purpose you know just to get them going. Don't you Dan?" And laughed as she walked by. Well no, he did not do it on purpose! He has dementia. As a caregiver, I was taken back by my co-worker's response. After getting Dan interested in a book about bears, I tracked her down and said "You know Dan really doesn't go after those girls just to get them riled up on purpose. It is the disease and his meds. I am sure that 10 years ago, it would upset him to no end thinking he would be where he is today because of this disease. So please try not to **encourage** *the behavior by thinking It's cute and he should do it again, because it's funny. It's not."*

Time To Go With It

The time is now . Join them in their world and their time, or you are fighting a losing battle. Give yourself permission to pretend you **understand** every mixed-up word they are saying. Let them repeat themselves and then act as if it is the first time you ever heard it. If you do, your life and theirs will be easier and much less stressful. **Encourage** them to keep **talking**, keep singing, keep walking and most of all to keep communicating with you, or if they can't, that's ok too.

Toileting

Your person will need assistance with their toileting. Barriers are gone, they may not know they need to go, how to wipe themselves, wash their hands even flush the toilet. They may fill the toilet with toilet paper, **food**, **clothing** the list goes on. You will end up having to guide them and even help them. **Caregivers** you hire for at home or in communities will assist with this.

Touching

They will touch everything, or anyone. It's all about touch and **feel**, pat and hold, making some type of connection. **Hand holding** can be a good solution, **hugs** are also amazing if you are both comfortable with it. Try to have things available that they can hold and examine, that are safe. Will they hold and cradle a baby doll? Will they adopt a stuffed dog or cat?

TV

This can be a wonderful resource for an activity. You have to be very careful. You may notice that certain shows or movies trigger certain responses. Does the news upset them to an unnatural level for them? Do certain types of movies give them nightmares? Make them sad or **cry**? Is a cop or medical show too realistic to them? Could it give them nightmares or really scare them? Remember they may not be able to decipher between fantasy or **reality**. If they see it, it can become their **reality**. Musicals are always a safe bet or comedies and game shows. Keep it dignified, stay away from cartoons unless this is what they enjoyed watching before the disease.

U

Understand

They need you, and need to know every moment they spend with you, that it is ok. They are ok. When they are at their worst state of confusion they will need to think that you understand. You get it, when no-one else does.

Dan enters the dining room, hands clasped behind his back. He surveys the crowd seated, and coming in to be seated. He chooses a table of ladies sitting together awaiting their **food***. Dan walks over stands very close to one of the ladies as there is no longer social barriers in place, smiles and he says "hello everyone." The ladies look up at him smile and say "hello." Dan smiles and moves over to the next table, repeating the salutation, hands still clasped behind his back. "What the hell do you want?" demands a lady who had a long career in the real estate. She is in a foul mood,* **agitated** *by the crowd and noise. "Well," Dan says "is everything ok?" leaning in concern furrowed in his brow (read body* **language***) "just get the hell out of here." The real estate agent snaps at him. Dan turns away from the table and slaps himself on the side of his head and begins to chant "I am bad, bad, bad. So stupid!" I rush to him and say Dan, Hello! I have been looking all over for you." I reach for his hand to hold it and stop the self-inflicted slaps. He looks at me and declares "I am bad, bad, bad!" then turns and gives a sour look at the real estate agent. I squeeze his hand drawing his attention back to me. "I have a project I need to do and I wanted to* **talk** *to you about it. Come sit over here where it is quiet and we can* **talk***." I begin to edge him away giving his hand a gentle pull. He follows me telling me he couldn't possibly help. He has too much going on, shaking his head. But he is following me and I sit with him at a quiet corner table. Dan used to be a principal, and I believe was working, trying to quiet the chaos, greeting the students, in his cafeteria duty.*

Use your Judgement

You will need to follow your gut feelings. You may need to make **decisions** that are hard and difficult. Taking their driver's license away. Insisting that your person needs help, or needs to move because they can no longer take care of themselves.

Knowing and accepting the fact, that you **love** your person enough to accept the challenge, of doing what is best for them, in your **judgement**. **Pray, breathe** and plunge ahead. Embrace the challenge, stand strong.

V

Validate

Tell them what a big help they have been. Let them do things with you or for you. Allow them to still feel important and **needed**. Thank them for helping you, for being your person. Remind them of their accomplishments in life, how important they are to you.

Violent

Violent behavior is the scariest behavior to deal with. Suddenly a small petite adorable senior can become a ball of **fury**, cussing, hitting, punching, scratching and biting. Breaking things, ripping things smashing things it can all happen. **Bait & Switch**, hand them a newspaper or magazine to rip and throw instead, something that doesn't matter, like laundry, but will just make a mess. Keep your **bubble** around you and stay out of reach. Chances are they will not hurt themselves, but anything else or anyone in the way, could bear the brunt of the violent behavior. You cannot afford to take that chance of getting hurt. Document the behavior and call the Doctor. It may be something that needs medication to control violent outbursts.

Vitamin Deficiency

When you begin to recognize those signs that something needs to be checked out by a doctor, you also want to pay attention to **food** intake. A vitamin deficiency can cause dementia symptoms. A good balanced diet can improve symptoms. If they have been **forgetting** to eat or how to cook, they most likely have forgotten to take their **medications**, or have not been taking them correctly. Try notes, hang picture signs, post a written schedule. Watch the fridge cupboards and the garbage.

W
Wait

Wait and wait some more. Everything is slower, the way your person walks, eats, and speaks. Give them the **dignity** to take their time to express themselves. Nothing can be fast, speech patterns are slow, the thought process is so disconnected for them it seems to take forever for them to answer the easiest **questions**, if they can at all. Giving them time to find the word they are trying to say is such a small priceless gift you can give to your person.

*We were doing our brain exercises and discussing the color of our first car. I asked Dan what color his first car was and he opened his mouth to respond, when the **words** just disappeared off his tongue. You could see the panic in his eyes as he desperately searched for the simple answer of blue. 5 seconds, 10, 15.... I smiled at him and said, I know you know Dan, Its ok. It will come to you, I **encouraged** him. 5 more seconds 10, 15 the other residents were getting restless. Do you see the color here, maybe my shirt (which was green) Dan searched the group his eyes resting on a lovely blue blouse that a resident was wearing. Taking the cue, I said Blue? He beamed at me nodded and said "Yes Blue. My favorite car was blue."*

Wandering

Not to be confused with an **escape artist**. Wandering happens when they are headed someplace but cannot remember where, or **why** they are going.

Maybe they are just "looking around". You hear news reports all the time about someone gone missing with dementia. This is terrifying for you both, you immediately and them when they realize they are lost. Time for you to look to local **resources** for help. They cannot be left alone any longer and their need for care and **supervision** just jumped to a whole new level. **Pray** for guidance. Kick in your **Sherlock**, arrange help from **family**, friends, **church** and do your research. Check out insurance coverage and **hire help** to come in and clean, cook take your person out on walks. Lock doors consider some type of alarm system. Make the calls to the Alzheimer's association for the support that is available in your community. Use the **internet**. **Ask** at **church**, there is a wealth of wisdom and knowledge there. Move them to a locked community where they can wander to their hearts content in a safe place.

Molly just walked everywhere. She never had a destination or **desperation** *when she walked. She just wandered. I would watch her peeking into rooms, occasionally shutting the door. She would try to open the occasional shut door if successful she would look inside and shut the door behind her. If the door was locked, she would move along until something else caught her attention. She wandered.*

Whistle

If you cannot **sing**, **hum** or **play an instrument**, try whistling. Instant soother.

Why

Who knows? God does, and he will give you the tools and skills to dance through this **dementia waltz**. You must have a little faith in Him, yourself and your person. You can face the hard choices and **decisions** you must make. Your person will lose the ability to explain **why** they did it, said it or felt that way. This is one word you can omit from your dementia vocabulary.

Wishes and Dreams

If your person has a wish or dream, and you can possibly make it happen, do it. Although **short term memory** is gone your person is very much in the moment. Is it Disney world? A visit to the old house they grew up in? To go to see a professional ball game?

*Dan was a retired air force pilot. A World War II veteran, and loved and missed flying his plane. I arranged for him and 10 members of his **family** (3 generations) to tour our local National Guard. He was given a coin of appreciation from the Major giving us the tour and sat at attention in his wheelchair during the whole presentation. We were shown current equipment that today's pilots have. The Major made it known to all of us that when Dan flew, none of this night vision high tech equipment was available. It was just Dan and the gages. The Major offered to have anyone try out the helmets and equipment, to which immediately Dan's son and grandson volunteered. Dan watched as helmets were put on and harness' were buckled. With pride, they stepped closer to Dan posing for him. Our tour Guide moved us out to the hanger where we got up close to the f-16's. Dan's eyes never left the planes, except to salute the pilots back as they saluted him. His family was so touched at his intent and alert response he had the minute he recognized where we were. We were invited to really check the plane out.*

*Dan's **family** climbed the tall ladder used to get into the cockpit. Dan of course could not get up there, but was watching closely as the others went up. I looked around and noticed that the back of the plane sat very low to the ground. "Dan," I whispered in his ear, "come with me for a minute." I wheeled him to the back of the plane where he reached out and ran his hand down the metal of the tail several times. "This was the best job I ever had." He beamed at me. I nodded in agreement and told him "yes I know."*

Word Salad

When the sentence being spoken makes no sense at all.

*"Hi Molly, did you have a cookie for desert?" She smiles, pats my arm and says "Well, I don't have cars in the bowl It had chips.". Word salad. "Yes," I agree " I **love** chocolate chips, my favorite!" She beams. "I'm glad! I'm am too!" She agrees. I did not **understand** everything she said, but more important I understood what she meant. I caught her drift.*

Words

It is ok to help your person find the word they are looking for. But only if your help is being accepted. If you are only adding to the **frustration** don't pursue it, try **bait & switch**. **Listen** to their word salad as if you are hanging onto every word.

X

Xceed

I am so lame but I needed something for you----Let them exceed at everything.

Molly hung out in the activity room from 1st thing in the morning until she went to bed. Her vision was fading, but she had a keen ear and could identify most by their voices. Molly loved it when we would play Bingo, she being the bingo caller. To hear her you would think she had been a professional. We had large laminated 8x11 cards with the letter and number printed for the whole room to see. Molly would peer at the card holding it only several inches from her face and in a big booming voice announce "B 3! I got beeee, threeee here folks b 3!" She would repeat herself until she was cued to go on to the next one, otherwise she would just holler out over and over. She used her most professional bingo caller voice, she shined with pride, exceeded my expectations!

Xplain

Over and over you will explain things or your person will try to explain things to you. You gotta lotta xplaining to do Lucy!

Y

Yesterday

It did not happen. It cannot be recalled. As the disease process continues your person won't remember yesterday or last week or last year. As personally heartbreaking as you feel during this period, something amazing will be the trade-off. Suddenly they will remember things from their young adulthood or childhood with clarity. Grab this opportunity and get to know this young person. She may suddenly become a **flirt** and shy at the same time. Or mischievous and funny. You will get to know your person as they once were. **Listen** and you will discover wonderful topics that you can use to guide your person to a warm happy place when they are having a bad time.

Youth

We always say that youth is wasted on the young. Your person will resort back to youthful times and days. You are their mother, aunt, grandmother even.

Z

Zen

The ultimate peaceful place that you and your person can reach on occasion that is stress free and beautiful. The **dementia waltz** will be the most difficult, stressful, lonely and sad and personal place you can ever be. It is heart wrenching and demanding, having to say goodbye to the person you used to know.

The beautiful side to that is there is an equally beautiful person that will emerge, a younger mind. The moments you will spend together can be funny, crazy, sad, enlightening, and oh so rewarding. You can guide your person through this challenging and demanding time yet reap the benefits of knowing so much more about your person as you **listen** to every word no matter how much sense it doesn't make. As you really look and read the **facial expressions**, body **language** and use the research you've done (and **Sherlock** you did your homework well), to keep your person **engaged.**

Zen, well it is the moments that you succeeded in letting your person know you were there, keeping them safe, loved. Calm. Happy. You **listened** to them and made a connection.

When you wiped away **tears** and you were clutched in a fierce bear hug. When they are giggling so hard that you must giggle too, when she can **sing** every single word of you are my sunshine, and harmonize the chorus. When **word salad** and repetitive sounds are her sentences. Zen is that rush of **love**, success and magic that you feel when it is good.

AFTERWORD

Do you need quick answers?

Are you looking for proven techniques to soothe someone you know with dementia?

Searching for ways to manage the behaviors and emotional challenges you and your person are facing through the disease process?

Are you looking for fast suggestions of managing life with someone suffering from dementia?

This book puts it in an alphabetical format for you to easily look up a specific suggestion for your easy reference, offering up ways to handle the hardest emotional challenges you are facing. Stories for you to read, things to try, ways to guide your person keeping their dignity and celebrating the person they are and who they will become. The stories may not fit your situation exactly. You will find ideas of how to manage some of your everyday challenges.

Look up a specific word, read the whole book from start to finish. It was written to help you *now*, as you join your person on their own dementia waltz, learning their own dance.

Take a deep breath and do some research. I hope you use this book often and you can also contact your local branch of the Alzheimer's Association. (ALZ.org), 24/7 Helpline 800-272-3900

Call them. Email them. Ask for help, resources, they will be glad to recommend in home health care agencies, independent/assisted/memory care/nursing home information, doctors, reading material, support groups. They will be one of your richest resources. I am donating part of the proceeds of the sale of this book to the Alzheimer's Association with hope that we can find a cure.

About the Author

Tammy grew up in Vermont and spent years learning how to manage living with someone with PTSD and all the emotional challenges, doctors and medication adjustments, while raising a blended family of seven. Her first career was in advertising, wanted a career change and over 16 years ago found a love of working with those with dementia. She became an LNA and Certified Dementia Practitioner during her career and continues to work in a memory care community. It became clear to her that so many of people find themselves in a caregiver position for someone in their life with no idea how to work through it. While recovering from a bad car accident she wrote this book for those beginning their own personal dementia waltz.

She offers no medical advice. That should always come from the doctors and medical professionals. It is her goal to simplify the dance for you, with time proven techniques and suggestions that you can use everyday to empower and validate your person and help you manage the many challenges you will face during this journey. This book is a reference guide with solutions spoken in simple terms, with stories to read for examples of how to handle some difficult situations. With the juggling of raising a family, friends and jobs taking on the responsibility of caregiving for a parent or spouse life is so very chaotic. Tammy hopes this book will help you become a bit more understanding, creative and empowered as you take care of yourself first.

NOTES AND NUMBERS

NOTES AND NUMBERS

56562383R00066

Made in the USA
Middletown, DE
22 July 2019